Es[sential] Skills for Reading Success:

Strategies
for Reading
Comprehension
and Test Taking
Revised

by Howard I. Berrent, Ph.D.
and Edward R. Nasello

RALLY! EDUCATION, LLC

Glen Head, New York

RALLY!
EDUCATI●N

We're all about student success!

ISBN 1-58380-994-5

Published 2004. Fifth Edition 2006
Printed in the U.S.A.

Cover Designer: Jean-Paul Vest
Book Designer: Lori Harley
Editorial Consultant: Eileen Gerard and Pat Keiserman
Illustrator, pages 6, 18, 38, 64, 96: Donna Stackhouse

RALLY! EDUCATION
22 Railroad Avenue
Glen Head, NY 11545
tel 888·99·RALLY
fax 516·671·7900
www.RALLYEDUCATION.com

Essential Skills for Reading Success
Strategies for Reading Comprehension and Test Taking

Table of Contents

Introduction

Welcome to *Essential Skills for Reading Success: Strategies for Reading Comprehension and Test Taking.* Being a successful reader means that you understand what you read. There are fourteen important skills you need to be a great reader. This book teaches you strategies, which are ways to use the skills when you read. It also teaches you how to answer reading comprehension questions on tests.

Essential Skills for Reading Success has different kinds of reading selections and different types of questions. You will read passages that are poems, and other passages that give you information, tell a story, or explain how to do something. You will be asked multiple-choice questions and questions that require you to write out an answer. When you finish this book you will be a better reader and a better test taker.

Essential Skills for Reading Success is made up of two parts:

Part A will teach you the essential reading comprehension skills one-by-one.

Part B will teach you the essential reading comprehension skills all together.

Throughout the book, we will provide *Strategies, Hints,* and *Reminders* to make learning easier for you. First we will model what we teach. Then we will guide you. Finally we will provide you with independent study to try on your own what you have learned.

When you finish *Essential Skills for Reading Success* you will be a better reader and a better test taker.

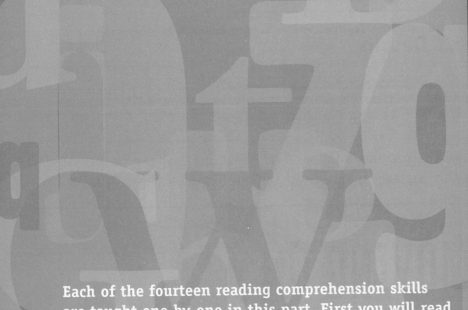

PART A

The 14 Essential Skills for Reading Success

One-by-One

Each of the fourteen reading comprehension skills are taught one-by-one in this part. First you will read a passage. You will then be asked some questions.

In **Modeled Instruction,** we will teach you a strategy that you can use to answer each question. Then we will explain each of the answer choices. We will show you why some of the choices are not correct. We will explain why the correct choice is the answer.

In **Guided Instruction,** we will provide *Hints* for you on how to answer the question. The first question will be multiple-choice. The second question will ask you to write out the answer.

In **Independent Study,** you will be on your own. You will answer multiple-choice and open-ended questions.

Skill 1: Recall Facts and Details

When answering questions based on a passage you must be able to remember information. These facts and details can be found in the passage. Often you will need to read the passage a second time to find the information you need to answer a question.

Directions: Read the passage below. The passage is followed by questions that can be answered by recalling facts and details. Use this passage to answer all the questions on pages 7–9.

MOVING ON

Mike was a lonely boy. He had just moved to a new town. He knew it was going to be very hard. Yet, Mike had no idea it was going to be this hard. He missed all his old friends. He missed playing video games with his best friend, Pete. He missed meeting his friend Kathleen on the playground after school. He missed riding his bicycle to school each day with his friends. He even missed his old school and Principal Saunders. About the only thing he didn't miss was the train that ran past his house every night. It was always hard to get a good night's sleep with the noise that the train made. Still Mike wished he could be back in his old house.

Mike's parents told him it would take time to adjust. Mike was not sure what they meant by saying that. He did not think he was ever going to adjust. His dog, Buddy, was the only friend he had in his new town. Even Buddy did not seem to like being there. He would not go outside to play fetch like he used to. When it was time to go to school, Mike would ride alone on his bike. At school he sat quietly. He did not talk to any of the other children.

After school one day, Mike's parents called him into the computer room. That's what they called the room in their new house that had the computer in it. His father asked him if he had ever heard of e-mail. Mike told his father that he had learned about e-mail at his new school. E-mail was a method of using computers to write letters to people. As Mike sat in front of the computer, his father showed him an e-mail. The e-mail was from his friend Pete. The e-mail said that all of the kids at the old school missed Mike. They agreed to keep in touch with each other by writing e-mails. Whenever Pete had some exciting news he would send Mike an e-mail. And whenever Mike had some exciting news he would send Pete an e-mail.

Over the next few months, Mike wrote back and forth with old friends through e-mail. At the same time, Mike began to feel more comfortable at his new school. He began to make new friends and no longer felt as lonely. Mike realized that he could still keep in touch with his old friends, but was happy to have new friends. Now Mike had even more friends than when he lived in his old town. Moving on does not have to be a bad thing, Mike thought to himself.

Modeled Instruction

Directions: Below is an example of a question that can be answered by recalling facts and details. Follow the strategy that is explained to help choose the correct answer.

> **1 Who is Mike's best friend?**
>
> Ⓐ Buddy
>
> Ⓑ Principal Saunders
>
> Ⓒ Pete
>
> Ⓓ Kathleen

Strategy: Use key words from the question to help you find where to look in the passage to find the answer. The key words for this question are "Mike's best friend." Read the parts of the passage that contain the key words. You should be able to find the facts and details that tell you what the correct answer is.

Use this strategy to decide which answer is correct.

 Ⓐ Buddy

The key word "friend" and the name "Buddy" can be found in the second paragraph. Details in this paragraph tell that Buddy is Mike's dog and is considered a friend. However, there are no details that suggest Buddy is Mike's best friend. Therefore, *choice "A" cannot be correct.*

 Ⓒ Pete

The key word "friend" and the name "Pete" can be found in both the first paragraph and the third paragraph. One sentence in the first paragraph states that Mike missed playing video games with his best friend, Pete. Therefore, *choice "C" must be the correct answer.*

 Ⓑ Principal Saunders

The key word "friend" and the name "Principal Saunders" can be found in the first paragraph. Details in this paragraph tell that Mike missed Principal Saunders but do not suggest Mike considers him a friend. Therefore, *choice "B" cannot be correct.*

 Ⓓ Kathleen

The key word "friend" and the name "Kathleen" can be found in the first paragraph. Details in this paragraph tell that Mike missed meeting his friend Kathleen on the playground after school. However, there are no details to suggest that Kathleen is Mike's best friend. Therefore, *choice "D" cannot be correct.*

Guided Instruction

Directions: Use the hints provided to answer the questions below. For question 2, you must choose the correct answer. For question 3, you will need to write out your answer.

2 What does Mike miss about his old town?

   Ⓐ the train

   Ⓑ his old school

   Ⓒ the computer room

   Ⓓ his bicycle

Hint: Use the key words "miss" and "old" to help find where in the passage the answer can be found. Read the part of the passage with these key words carefully to find the details needed to answer the question.

3 When will Mike and Pete send each other e-mail?

Hint: The third and fourth paragraphs contain the key word "e-mail." The third paragraph also contains the key words "Pete" and "Mike." Read these paragraphs again to find the details needed to answer the question.

Independent Study

Directions: Answer the following questions on your own. For questions 4, 5, and 6, choose the correct answer. For question 7, you must write out your answer.

4 What room did Mike's parents call him into?

Ⓐ the computer room

Ⓑ the bedroom

Ⓒ the kitchen

Ⓓ the dining room

6 How did Mike get to his new school?

Ⓐ His parents drove him.

Ⓑ He took the bus.

Ⓒ He rode his bicycle.

Ⓓ He walked alone.

5 How did Mike learn about e-mail?

Ⓐ He learned about it from his father.

Ⓑ He learned about it from his friends.

Ⓒ He learned about it at his old school.

Ⓓ He learned about it at his new school.

7 Why doesn't Mike miss the train that ran past his house every night?

_____

_____

_____

_____

_____

_____

_____

_____

_____

_____

_____

_____

_____

_____

_____

_____

Skill 2: Identify Main Idea

The main idea is what the whole passage is about. To identify the main idea of a passage, you must think about all of the information in the passage. When a passage tells about more than one thing you must ask yourself what it is mostly about. Some questions may ask you to tell the main idea of a paragraph or a sentence. To answer those questions you only need to think about what the paragraph or sentence is about.

Directions: Read the passage below. The passage is followed by questions that can be answered by identifying main ideas. Use this passage to answer all the questions on pages 11–13.

Many different countries make up Europe. Great Britain, France, and Spain are countries that many people think of when they think about Europe. There are other interesting countries that also make up Europe. One of those countries is Finland. As a matter of fact, Finland is the fifth largest country in Europe.

Finland is bordered by Russia, Norway, and Sweden. Finland has many lakes and rivers. It is also a country covered with much forest. In fact, 65% of the land in Finland is forest. People in Finland make great use of their forests. The country's economy relies heavily on the timber industry. The timber industry harvests wood from trees to sell or use in many different ways.

The capital of Finland is Helsinki. Helsinki is also Finland's largest city. More than 500,000 people live in Helsinki. More than 5 million people live in Finland. This is about the same number of people who live in New York City.

Like the United States and many other countries, Finland has a constitution. The laws that the people of Finland must follow are in their constitution. They adopted their constitution in 1919. The people of Finland also elect a president. Unlike the United States, the president of Finland serves terms of six years. The president of the United States serves terms of four years.

People first arrived in Finland over 7,000 years ago. Over the last two hundred years, the people of Finland have had to fight for their country. Finland has fought wars with both Russia and Sweden to keep or regain their independence. Since World War II, Finland has remained neutral and tried to stay out of wars. With a history longer than the United States, Finland is a country worth learning more about.

NORWAY
SWEDEN
FINLAND
Helsinki
RUSSIA
GREAT BRITAIN
Baltic Sea
GERMANY
FRANCE
SPAIN
Mediterranean Sea

PART A: The 14 Essential Skills for Reading Success — One-by-One

Modeled Instruction

Directions: Below is an example of a question that can be answered by identifying the main idea of the passage. Follow the strategy that is explained to help choose the correct answer.

---

1 **What would be the best title for this passage?**

(A) *Finland and the United States*

(B) *The Nations of Europe*

(C) *A New Nation Is Born*

(D) *All about Finland*

Strategy: A good title can tell a reader the main idea of a passage. You need to think about all of the information you read to tell what the main idea of the passage is. Ask yourself, "What is the passage mostly about?"

Use this strategy to decide which answer is correct.

 (A) **Finland and the United States**

The third paragraph does tell about Finland and the United States, but Finland is mentioned in the other paragraphs. Since the passage does not give much information about the United States, *choice "A" cannot be correct.*

 (C) **A New Nation Is Born**

The passage does give information about the history of Finland, but only the last paragraph tells about the birth of this nation. Since the passage only gives a few details about how Finland became a nation, *choice "C" cannot be the correct answer.*

 (B) **The Nations of Europe**

Many nations in Europe are mentioned within the passage, but most of the details given are only about Finland. Since the passage does not give much information about the other nations in Europe, *choice "B" cannot be correct.*

 (D) **All about Finland**

Finland is mentioned in every paragraph of the passage. Each paragraph gives details and facts about the country. Since the passage is mostly about Finland, *choice "D" must be the correct answer.*

Guided Instruction

Directions: Use the hints provided to answer the questions below. For question 2, you must choose the correct answer. For question 3, you will need to write out your answer.

---

2 The second paragraph in the passage tells mostly about—

- Ⓐ the land and resources of Finland
- Ⓑ the lakes and rivers of Finland
- Ⓒ the countries that border Finland
- Ⓓ the people of Finland

Hint: To answer this question you need to look only at the second paragraph. Think about what important facts can be found in this paragraph. Ask yourself what most of these facts tell you about.

---

3 What is the third paragraph mainly about? Remember to list facts and details that support your main idea.

_____

_____

_____

_____

_____

_____

_____

_____

_____

_____

_____

_____

_____

_____

_____

_____

Hint: Think about the facts and details that are given in the third paragraph. What are all the details describing? What are these facts and details telling you about? This is the main idea. Include this information in your answer.

Independent Study

Directions: Answer the following questions on your own. For questions 4, 5, and 6, choose the correct answer. For question 7, you must write out your answer.

4 This passage is *mostly* about—

  Ⓐ the people of Finland

  Ⓑ the nations of Europe

  Ⓒ the people of Europe

  Ⓓ the country of Finland

5 What is the main idea of the fourth paragraph in the passage?

  Ⓐ Finland's constitution

  Ⓑ how the United States and Finland are alike

  Ⓒ what the government of Finland is like

  Ⓓ how Finland elects its President

6 Which fact below would fit best in the first paragraph of the passage?

  Ⓐ Europe is one of seven continents in the world.

  Ⓑ Vantaa and Espoo are cities in Finland.

  Ⓒ Lakes and rivers cover about 10% of Finland.

  Ⓓ World War II ended in the year 1945.

7 Write your own summary about the passage on page 10. Remember to include the main ideas of each paragraph in your summary.

Skill 3: Identify Sequence

To identify sequence means to be able to place information or things that have happened in the correct order. To answer questions about sequence you must read the passage to find out when actions or events occur. You must be able to find out at what point in time something happened.

Directions: Read the passage below. The passage is followed by questions that can be answered by identifying sequence. Use this passage to answer all the questions on pages 15–17.

COME VISIT OAKDALE PETTING ZOO!

- RIDE TONY THE PONY -
- PET PETE THE PARROT -
- FEED GILDA THE GOAT -

Park is open Monday through Friday.
Petting Zoo hours: 9:00 A.M. – 6:00 P.M.

DAILY SHOW SCHEDULE
(All shows are 20 minutes long.)

9:30 A.M.   Birds of Paradise
Get an up-close look at parrots, macaws, and tucans. Watch as these birds perform amazing tricks.

11:00 A.M.   Penny the Pig and Friends
Laugh out loud and enjoy the comical adventures of Penny the Pig and her friends. This show features some of the best trained animals in all of Oakdale.

1:30 P.M.   The Big Parade!
Line up along Animal Alley and wave to your favorite animals. Ponies, pigs, goats, and geese march to the beat of the drums and the blare of the bugles. Get up close and take great photos!

4:45 P.M.   Animal Antics
Meet our staff of trainers and their animal companions by the main gate. You will have a chance to teach animals new tricks—our trainers will show you how.

Daily Lunch Special!
Meet in the main cafeteria between 11:15 A.M. and 2:00 P.M. and eat all you can for only $5 per person.

Gift Shop
Before leaving the Petting Zoo be sure to visit the gift shop for a special gift. The gift shop opens at 10:30 A.M. and remains open until the Zoo closes.

Fireworks Finale   ALL NEW SHOW!!!
Gather at the lake to see an amazing display of fireworks. Fireworks begin at 9:15 P.M. *Thursdays only!*

Directions to the Petting Zoo:
- Take Route 15 to Exit 29.
- Turn right when getting off at Exit 29.
- Go five blocks to the first traffic light.
- At the traffic light turn left onto Main St.
- At the second stop sign on Main St. turn right onto Davis Ave.
- Go one block on Davis Ave. and look for the Oakdale Petting Zoo on your right.

Park hours: 9:00 A.M. – 10:00 P.M.

For additional information call our main office at 555-7766. Office hours are from 8:00 A.M. to 5:00 P.M.

To purchase tickets in advance, call the sales office at 1-888-555-4545. The sales office is open from 7:00 A.M. to 8:00 P.M.

Modeled Instruction

Directions: Below is an example of a question that can be answered by identifying the sequence of events. Follow the strategy that is explained to help choose the correct answer.

---

1 Which show starts before the daily lunch special begins and after the gift shop opens?

(A) Birds of Paradise

(B) Penny the Pig and Friends

(C) The Big Parade!

(D) Animal Antics

Strategy: To answer questions that require identifying sequence it can be helpful to create a timeline. Read the passage and look for key times or dates to help you determine when things happen. You should complete this timeline before you answer the question.

9:00 A.M.	Park opens
10:00 A.M.	
11:00 A.M.	
12:00 P.M.	
1:00 P.M.	
2:00 P.M.	
3:00 P.M.	
4:00 P.M.	
5:00 P.M.	
6:00 P.M.	

Use this strategy to decide which answer is correct.

 (A) Birds of Paradise

The daily lunch special begins at 11:15 A.M. and the gift shop opens at 10:30 A.M. The Birds of Paradise show begins at 9:30 A.M. Since this show begins before the gift shop opens, *choice "A" cannot be correct.*

 (C) The Big Parade!

The Big Parade begins at 1:30 P.M. The daily lunch special begins at 11:15 A.M. Since the parade starts after the lunch special begins, *choice "C" cannot be correct.*

 (B) Penny the Pig and Friends

Penny the Pig and Friends starts at 11:00 A.M. This is after the gift shop opens at 10:30 A.M. and before the daily lunch special begins at 11:15 A.M. Therefore, *choice "B" is the correct answer.*

 (D) Animal Antics

The Animal Antics show begins at 4:45 P.M. The daily lunch special begins at 11:15 A.M. Since this show starts after the lunch special begins, *choice "D" cannot be correct.*

Guided Instruction

Directions: Use the hints provided to answer the questions below. For question 2, you must choose the correct answer. For question 3, you will need to write out your answer.

2 Which of the following opens first?

Ⓐ the Petting Zoo

Ⓑ the gift shop

Ⓒ the main office

Ⓓ the sales office

Hint: Look at the information given to find the time at which each event occurs. Use this information in your timeline of events to answer this question. Ask yourself which event occurs first.

3 List three things you could do at the Petting Zoo if you arrived at 1:00 P.M.

_____

_____

_____

_____

_____

_____

_____

_____

_____

_____

_____

_____

_____

_____

_____

_____

_____

Hint: Identify all of the events that begin after 1:00 P.M. You must also look for events that end after 1:00 P.M. Be sure to consider things you could do besides seeing shows.

Independent Study

Directions: Answer the following questions on your own. For questions 4, 5, and 6, choose the correct answer. For question 7, you must write out your answer.

4 Look at the timeline below.

Which of the following should be placed in the empty box to complete the timeline?

(A) the lunch special ends

(B) the gift shop closes

(C) the Penny the Pig show begins

(D) the Big Parade finishes

5 When going to the Petting Zoo, what must you do before turning left onto Main Street?

(A) turn right when getting off at Exit 29

(B) go to the second stop sign and turn right

(C) look for the Oakdale Petting Zoo on your right

(D) go one block on Davis Avenue

6 What is the first show that you could go to after the daily lunch special has ended?

(A) Birds of Paradise

(B) Penny the Pig and Friends

(C) The Big Parade!

(D) Animal Antics

7 What things could you do at the Petting Zoo between the time the gift shop opens and the Animal Antics show begins? Describe three things you could do in the order you would do them.

_____

_____

_____

_____

_____

_____

_____

_____

_____

_____

_____

_____

_____

Skill 4: Analyze Language and Vocabulary

To analyze language you must look at the words, phrases, and sentences and how they are used in a passage. Sometimes you will be asked to tell what the words mean. At other times you may need to explain how words are used to express ideas or to tell a story.

Directions: Read the poem below. The poem is followed by questions that can be answered by analyzing words, phrases, and sentences. Use this poem to answer all the questions on pages 19–21.

Pirate Story

by Robert Louis Stevenson

1	Three of us afloat in the meadow by the swing,
2	Three of us *abroad* in the basket on the lea.
3	Winds are in the air, they are blowing in the spring,
4	And waves are on the meadow like the waves there are at sea.
5	Where shall we adventure, to-day that we're *afloat,*
6	Wary of the weather, and steering by a star?
7	Shall it be to Africa, a-steering of the boat,
8	To Providence, or Babylon, or off to *Malaba*r?
9	Hi! But there's a *squadron* a-rowing on the sea—
10	Cattle on the meadow a-charging with a roar!
11	Quick, and we'll escape them, they're as mad as they can be,
12	The wicket is the harbor and the garden is the shore.

Modeled Instruction

Directions: Below is an example of a question that can be answered by analyzing language in the poem. Follow the strategy that is explained to help choose the correct answer.

<table>
<tr><td>

1 In line 2 the word *abroad* means—

(A) flying

(B) angry

(C) beneath

(D) traveling

</td></tr>
</table>

Strategy: Thinking about how a word is used in a sentence can help you to understand its meaning. Some words in a sentence can give you clues about the meaning of other words. Sometimes you may need to look at a few sentences and how they fit together in order to discover the meaning of a word. The word *abroad* is in the first stanza, or part, of the poem.

Use this strategy to decide which answer is correct.

 (A) flying

The poem tells about an imaginary adventure at sea. You would be floating, not flying if you were traveling at sea. Therefore, *choice "A" does not appear to give the best possible meaning for the word.*

 (C) beneath

The word abroad is followed by "in the basket." It does not make sense to be "beneath in the basket." Therefore, *choice "C" does not appear to give the best possible meaning for the word.*

 (B) angry

Being angry does not fit with being on an exciting adventure. There are no words or sentences that suggest anyone is angry. Therefore, *choice "B" does not appear to give the best possible meaning for the word.*

 (D) traveling

Details about the imaginary adventure are "winds are in the air" and a "meadow by the swing." These details suggest that this is a traveling adventure. Since the word "traveling" seems to fit best, *choice "D" is the correct answer.*

Guided Instruction

Directions: Use the hints provided to answer the questions below. For question 2, you must choose the correct answer. For question 3, you will need to write out your answer.

---

2 **The phrase "waves are on the meadow like the waves there are at sea" suggests—**

(A) you can see waves on a meadow

(B) saying goodbye in a meadow is like saying goodbye at sea

(C) the grass in the field looks like waves on the water

(D) the waves water makes can be used in a field

Hint: Compare the group of words in each answer choice with the words in the question. Which answer choice has the same meaning as the words in the question?

---

3 **What do you think the phrase "wary of the weather" means?**

_____

_____

_____

_____

_____

_____

_____

_____

_____

_____

_____

_____

_____

_____

Hint: Read the part of the poem where this phrase is used. What do the details tell you about how the characters in the poem might feel about the weather? If you were at sea how would you feel about the weather?

Independent Study

Directions: Answer the following questions on your own. For questions 4, 5, and 6, choose the correct answer. For question 7, you must write out your answer.

4 *Malabar* is the name of—

Ⓐ a place

Ⓑ a person

Ⓒ an animal

Ⓓ a food

5 Which word helps the reader know what the word *afloat* means?

Ⓐ basket

Ⓑ waves

Ⓒ wind

Ⓓ swing

6 Read the different meanings for the word *squadron.*

1. a large group

2. a troop of soldiers

3. a group of planes

4. a group of ships

Which meaning best fits the way the word *squadron* is used in line 9?

Ⓐ meaning 1

Ⓑ meaning 2

Ⓒ meaning 3

Ⓓ meaning 4

7 In line 6 what does the author mean by "steering by a star"?

_____

_____

_____

_____

_____

_____

_____

_____

_____

_____

_____

Skill 5: Analyze Character, Plot, and Setting

To analyze character, plot, and setting you must be able to describe each one based on information in the passage.

CHARACTER	**who** the passage is about
PLOT	**what** the passage is about
SETTING	**where** and **when** the events take place

Directions: Read the passage below. The passage is followed by questions that can be answered by analyzing the characters, plot, and setting. Use this passage to answer all the questions on pages 23–25.

A Day in the Life of Jake

The sun shined through the window onto the living room floor. Jake could feel its warmth on his back. Lying on the floor, Jake lifted his head and looked out the window. Slowly he sat up. He did not move for several minutes. Then he lifted his back paw and began to scratch his ear. As he scratched his ear he heard the bedroom door open and the sound of footsteps. As Jake began to make his way to the kitchen, he looked up and saw Jamal.

"Come here, boy!" Jamal called out.

Jamal bent down to pat Jake and scratch him behind his ears. Jake loved it when Jamal scratched him behind his ears—it was one of his favorite things. The two walked into the kitchen together. Jamal filled one bowl with water and another with "doggie bits." Jake loved doggie bits. As far as Jake was concerned, the only thing better than doggie bits was a bone. Jake wagged his tail as he cleaned the bowl with his tongue. He then washed down the doggie bits with some cold water.

"Wanna go out?" Jamal asked as he opened the back door.

Jake sprinted to the backyard and ran across the grass. He ran back and forth across the yard several times. It was truly a great start to a new day. Then Jake stopped in his tracks as he heard a sound.

"Meow," Jake heard coming from the other side of the fence.

It was Phoebe and Penelope. Jake ran to the wooden fence at the back of the yard. He peeked through an opening to be sure it was them. Peeking back at him was Phoebe.

Jake began to bark and scratch the fence frantically. Phoebe took a step back and hissed at Jake. Soon Penelope joined in and began to hiss too. The barking and hissing continued for several minutes.

Then Jamal walked over to Jake and showed him a chewed-up orange ball. "Go fetch," Jamal said as he tossed the ball across the yard away from the fence. Without hesitating Jake chased after the ball. Then he brought it back to Jamal and dropped it at his feet. Jake loved playing fetch with Jamal. He loved it so much that he already had forgotten about Phoebe and Penelope.

Later in the day while Jamal was playing soccer with his friends, his younger sister, Yvette, played with Jake. Yvette was three years old and just the right size to climb on Jake's back. Jake didn't mind being treated as if he were a horse. But he did not like it when Yvette pulled on his tail. He also didn't like it when she put a paper bag on his head.

Jake and Yvette played together in the yard all afternoon. Soon it was time for dinner. Jake could hardly wait to see what was in his bowl. As soon as the back door opened, Jake charged into the house and made his way to the kitchen. Waiting for him was a large bone and a bowl of water. Jake began to wag his tail as he noticed several pieces of meat that were still on the bone. Jake began eating. A few feet away Jamal, Yvette, and Mr. and Mrs. Vernon sat at a table and ate their dinner.

After dinner, Jake snuggled up against Jamal's legs as the entire Vernon family sat on the living room couch reading stories to each other. This was Jake's favorite time of day. He could not understand the words he heard as they read to each other, but he liked the way they sounded. Soon it was time for bed.

The children gave their mother and father a kiss, then went off to bed. Mr. Vernon locked the doors to the house and closed the windows. Mrs. Vernon walked into each room and turned off the lights. The last light that needed to be turned off was the one next to the couch. Mrs. Vernon bent down on one knee and pat Jake on the head. "Good night Jake," she said before turning off the light.

A few minutes later Jake was sound asleep dreaming about playing fetch in the backyard with Jamal.

Modeled Instruction

Directions: Below is an example of a question that can be answered by analyzing character, plot, and setting in the passage. Follow the strategy that is explained to help choose the correct answer.

1 Where does part of the story take place?

  Ⓐ in the kitchen

  Ⓑ in the basement

  Ⓒ in Jamal's bedroom

  Ⓓ in Yvette's bedroom

Strategy: To analyze character, plot, and setting it can be helpful to organize details in a story. You can use a story map to sort out who does what, as well as what the story is about. It can also help you explore where and when events in the story take place. This question is asking you about the setting.

Use this strategy to decide which answer is correct.

 Ⓐ in the kitchen

Different events in the story occur in different places. When Jake is eating and drinking from his bowl he is in the kitchen. Therefore, *choice "A" can be the correct answer.*

 Ⓒ in Jamal's bedroom

One part of the story does mention that Jake can hear Jamal coming out of his bedroom. However, no action in the story actually takes place in this room. Therefore, *choice "C" cannot be correct.*

 Ⓑ in the basement

Different parts of the story take place in different rooms within the house. However, there is no mention of anything happening in the basement. Therefore, *choice "B" cannot be correct.*

 Ⓓ in Yvette's bedroom

One line near the end of the passage explains that the children "went off to bed." However, there is no mention of anything happening in this room. Therefore, *choice "D" cannot be correct.*

Guided Instruction

Directions: Use the hints provided to answer the questions below. For question 2, you must choose the correct answer. For question 3, you will need to write out your answer.

2 **What can you tell about Jamal from reading the passage?**

Ⓐ He does not like cats.

Ⓑ He does not like dogs.

Ⓒ He likes to play baseball.

Ⓓ He likes to play soccer.

Hint: Think about Jamal's actions in the passage. The things that a character does or says can tell you a lot about him or her. This is a character question.

3 **Summarize what this passage is about. Explain what happens in the beginning, middle, and end of the story.**

_____

_____

_____

_____

_____

_____

_____

_____

_____

_____

_____

_____

_____

_____

_____

_____

_____

Hint: To summarize the plot of a passage you need to explain only about important details and events. Think about what information is important.

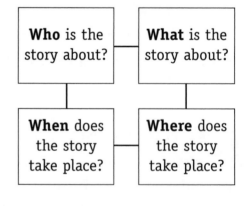

Who is the story about?	**What** is the story about?
When does the story take place?	**Where** does the story take place?

Independent Study

Directions: Answer the following questions on your own. For questions 4, 5, and 6, choose the correct answer. For question 7, you must write out your answer.

4 Jake can *best* be described as—

Ⓐ fast

Ⓑ playful

Ⓒ lonely

Ⓓ smart

5 Where is Jake when the story begins and ends?

Ⓐ in the living room

Ⓑ in the backyard

Ⓒ in the kitchen

Ⓓ in the bedroom

6 Which two characters in the story are most alike?

Ⓐ Jake and Phoebe

Ⓑ Jamal and Yvette

Ⓒ Phoebe and Penelope

Ⓓ Jake and Yvette

7 How would you describe Jamal? Include two examples that show what type of person he is.

_____

_____

_____

_____

_____

_____

_____

_____

_____

_____

_____

_____

_____

Cause and effect questions ask about events that are connected to each other in some way.

CAUSE	the event that leads to the effect—*The wind is blowing hard.*
EFFECT	the result of the event—*The tree falls down.*

Directions: Read the passage below. The passage is followed by questions that can be answered by recognizing cause and effect. Use this passage to answer all the questions on pages 27–29.

CORAL 🪸 REEFS

Coral reefs provide homes to a countless number of creatures in the ocean. A fish such as an eel can hide in its cracks and crevices waiting for a meal to swim by. Sponges and anemones cover its surface and feed on the tiny remains of the eel's victim. Dolphins and sharks swim by for a visit and feed on the many fish that make the reef their home. Coral reefs are very important to our oceans.

Coral reefs are created by tiny animals called polyps. These polyps live in large groups called colonies. They take calcium out of the seawater. The calcium then forms a limestone deposit around the lower half of the polyp. As the colony of polyps grows, the limestone formations also continue to grow. Over the course of thousands of years large coral reefs are formed. As these reefs form, small animals that live in the ocean use them for shelter. Soon, bigger animals come to the reef to feed on these smaller animals. Before long there is an entire colony of ocean life.

Sometimes a reef builds up so much that it is above the water. When this happens soil can be deposited on the reef. If this happens vegetation begins to grow. Over time an island is created. Many islands in the Pacific were formed this way.

Coral reefs have attracted great attention. Many people enjoy swimming near reefs to look at the variety of sea creatures that live there. Unfortunately, there have been some harmful effects. Many divers have broken off pieces to take home as souvenirs. Sometimes boats crash into reefs and cause damage.

In an effort to protect coral reefs, laws have been created. Some laws have made it illegal to collect or destroy coral in parts of the world. Also, preserves have been established. A preserve is a place that is protected.

There are some threats to coral reefs that little can be done about. For example, tropical storms and hurricanes can be harmful. The strong wave action they cause often damages reefs. Also, if the sea level rises it can cause problems. As the water rises the amount of sunlight that reaches the reef decreases. This slows down reef growth.

In recent years people have tried to help create reefs. This has been done by using "reef balls." Reef balls are igloo-shaped domes made from concrete. When placed in the ocean under the

proper conditions polyps will attach themselves. Over time it is hoped that new reefs will form.
Coral reefs can be found all around the world. They are very important to our oceans. To protect coral reefs requires special care and commitment from everyone.

Modeled Instruction

Directions: Below is an example of a question that can be answered by recognizing cause and effect. Follow the strategy that is explained to help choose the correct answer.

---

1 What can cause an island to form?

Ⓐ when coral reefs are destroyed

Ⓑ when sponges and anemones cover the surface of a reef

Ⓒ when the reef builds up so much that it is above water

Ⓓ when there is strong wave action in the water

Strategy: Look for key words in the question to help you figure out where to look in the passage for your answer. If the question gives you the cause, then you must find the effect or what happens. If the question gives you the effect, then you must find the cause.

Use this strategy to decide which answer is correct.

 Ⓐ **when coral reefs are destroyed**

The third paragraph tells about how islands are formed. It does not mention anything about coral reefs being destroyed. Therefore, *choice "A" cannot be correct.*

 Ⓑ **when sponges and anemones cover the surface of a reef**

Sponges and anemones are mentioned in the first paragraph, but nothing in this part of the passage indicates that they cause the islands to be formed. Therefore, *choice "B" cannot be correct.*

 Ⓒ **when the reef builds up so much that it is above water**

The third paragraph explains that when a reef builds up above the water soil is sometimes deposited. It also explains that vegetation will grow in this soil and over time an island may be created. Therefore, *choice "C" is the correct answer.*

 Ⓓ **when there is strong wave action in the water**

The sixth paragraph explains that strong wave action can cause damage to coral reefs. It does not mention anything about how islands are created. Therefore, *choice "D" is not correct.*

Guided Instruction

Directions: Use the hints provided to answer the questions below. For question 2, you must choose the correct answer. For question 3, you will need to write out your answer.

2   What will happen if a reef ball is placed in the ocean?

Ⓐ Under the proper conditions polyps will attach themselves.

Ⓑ Under the proper conditions it will leave limestone deposits.

Ⓒ It will cause damage to coral reefs.

Ⓓ It will protect coral reefs.

Hint: Placing a reef ball in the ocean is the cause of something. Look through the passage to find what the effect is. Look for the key words "reef ball" to help you find the part of the passage where this information can be found.

3   What causes the limestone formations that make a reef grow?

_____

_____

_____

_____

_____

_____

_____

_____

_____

_____

_____

_____

_____

_____

_____

Hint: Limestone formations are the effect of something else that happens. Look through the passage to find the details that explain what causes this.

Independent Study

Directions: Answer the following questions on your own. For questions 4, 5, and 6, choose the correct answer. For question 7, you must write out your answer.

---

4 **What happens when small animals that live in the ocean use a reef for shelter?**

Ⓐ The reef is damaged by these fish.

Ⓑ Bigger animals come to the reef to feed on these animals.

Ⓒ Soil can be deposited on the reef.

Ⓓ They take calcium out of the water and make limestone deposits.

---

6 **If an eel eats another fish—**

Ⓐ coral polyps will feed on the tiny remains

Ⓑ sponges and anemones will feed on the tiny remains

Ⓒ dolphins and sharks will feed on the tiny remains

Ⓓ more eels will feed on the tiny remains

---

5 **Why have ocean preserves been established?**

Ⓐ to attract people to coral reefs

Ⓑ to attract fish to coral reefs

Ⓒ to protect coral reefs from being damaged by people

Ⓓ to protect coral reefs from being damaged by fish

---

7 **What causes damage to a reef? Explain at least two causes discussed in the passage on page 26.**

_____

_____

_____

_____

_____

_____

_____

_____

_____

_____

_____

_____

_____

Skill 7: Compare and Contrast

To compare means that you must tell how things are alike. To contrast means that you must tell how things are different. Compare and contrast questions may ask you to compare or contrast people, things, places, or events.

Directions: Read the passage below. The passage is followed by questions that can be answered by comparing or contrasting. Use this passage to answer all the questions on pages 31–33.

PLANNING THE TRIP

For a long time Javier and his mom had discussed going away during his summer break. They had talked about many different options. His mother thought that it would be nice to travel around to different baseball parks. However, as Javier grew older, baseball had become less of an interest. She suggested that they go to Disney World, but Javier didn't like that idea either. Javier was a real nature lover. He also loved trying new things.

So, one night during dinner, Javier had the idea to drive around the country visiting as many national parks as possible. They lived in the northeast. Javier wanted to visit parks that were in other parts of the country. The next day he got a book from the library to look at some options. Here is a list of parks that he wrote down for his mom to look at.

ARCHES NATIONAL PARK
Moab, Utah
Established 1929
Facilities: campground, picnic areas, museum
Activities: camping, hiking, guided tours
Special Features: giant arches, pinnacles, sandstone walls called "fins"; pedestals that change color constantly as the sun moves overhead.

BANDELIER NATIONAL MONUMENT
Los Alamos, New Mexico
Established 1932
Facilities: campground, picnic area, groceries, museum
Activities: camping, hiking, fishing, guided tours
Special Features: canyon-slashed slopes of Pajarito Plateau; cliff house ruins of the 13th-century Pueblo Indians.

BADLANDS NATIONAL PARK
Interior, South Dakota
Established 1929
Facilities: campground, cabin rental, restaurant, museum
Activities: hiking, camping, wildlife viewing
Special Features: scenic landscape; animal fossils that date back 40 million years; prairie grasslands that support bison, bighorn sheep, deer and antelope.

BLUE RIDGE PARKWAY
Ashville, North Carolina
Established 1933
Facilities: campground, backcountry use permits, boat rentals, horseback riding
Activities: hiking, fishing, horseback riding, snowmobiling, skiing, camping
Special Features: scenic parkway that averages 3,000 feet above sea level; Blue Ridge Mountains; more than 1,000 bird species can been seen during the spring season.

Modeled Instruction

Directions: Below is an example of a question that can be answered by comparing and contrasting information in the passage. Follow the strategy that is explained to help choose the correct answer.

---

1 Which activities take place at all four national parks?

Ⓐ camping and guided tours

Ⓑ camping and hiking

Ⓒ skiing and hiking

Ⓓ skiing and fishing

Strategy: Making lists can help you to compare and contrast. You can make one list that tells how things are alike and another to tell how they are different. These lists can be used to help answer questions that ask you to compare or contrast.

	Alike	Different
Park 1		
Park 2		
Park 3		
Park 4		

Use this strategy to decide which answer is correct.

 Ⓐ camping and guided tours

Camping is listed as an activity at all four parks, but guided tours is listed as an activity only at Arches National Park and Bandelier National Monument. Since both activities are not listed for all four parks, *choice "A" cannot be correct.*

 Ⓒ skiing and hiking

Hiking is listed as an activity at all four parks, but skiing is listed as an activity only at Blue Ridge Parkway. Since both activities are not listed for all four parks, *choice "C" cannot be correct.*

 Ⓑ camping and hiking

Camping is listed as an activity at all four parks. Hiking is also listed as an activity at all four parks. Therefore, *choice "B" must be the correct answer.*

 Ⓓ skiing and fishing

Neither skiing nor fishing is listed as an activity at all four parks. Therefore, *choice "D" cannot be correct.*

Guided Instruction

Directions: Use the hints provided to answer the questions below. For question 2, you must choose the correct answer. For question 3, you will need to write out your answer.

---

2 What is one way in which Badlands National Park is different from Arches National Park?

Ⓐ It is located out west.

Ⓑ It was established in 1929.

Ⓒ It has a campground.

Ⓓ It is located in South Dakota.

Hint: All of the details listed are true, but only one tells how the parks are different. Read the details about each park again. Which detail is true about Badlands National Park, but NOT true about Arches National Park? You can make a Venn Diagram to help you answer this question or you can use the chart that you made for question 1.

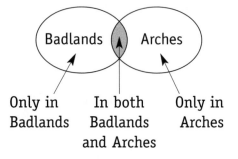

Only in Badlands   In both Badlands and Arches   Only in Arches

---

3 How are Bandelier National Monument and Badlands National Park alike?

_____

_____

_____

_____

_____

_____

_____

_____

_____

Hint: Read the information given about each place. Compare the facilities, activities, and special features that can be found at both places. Tell how the two are alike.

Independent Study

Directions: Answer the following questions on your own. For questions 4, 5, and 6, choose the correct answer. For question 7, you must write out your answer.

4 Which two national parks were established in the same year?

(A) Arches National Park and Badlands National Park

(B) Arches National Park and Bandelier National Monument

(C) Blue Ridge Parkway and Badlands National Park

(D) Blue Ridge Parkway and Bandelier National Monument

5 Which of the following can be found at both Badlands National Park and Blue Ridge Parkway?

(A) a scenic parkway

(B) animals

(C) a museum

(D) snowmobiles

6 How are the facilities at Bandelier National Monument and Arches National Park different?

(A) Bandelier National Monument has a campground, but Arches National Park does not.

(B) Arches National Park has a picnic area, but Bandelier National Monument does not.

(C) Bandelier National Monument has a place to get groceries, but Arches National Park does not.

(D) Arches National Park has a museum, but Bandelier National Monument does not.

7 How are Arches National Park and Blue Ridge Parkway different from each other?

_____

_____

_____

_____

_____

_____

_____

_____

_____

_____

A

Skill 8: Distinguish Fact from Opinion

To answer some questions you must be able to identify which statements are facts and which are opinions. For example:

FACT a statement that **is true**—*There are 50 states in the United States.*

OPINION a statement that someone **believes is true**—*My state is the most beautiful.*

Directions: Read the passage below. The passage is followed by questions that can be answered by distinguishing fact from opinion. Use this passage to answer all the questions on pages 35–37.

School-wide Update:

Now on the Menu... Fruit!

Good News! Starting next Monday the school lunch menu will include some new snack foods. No, not potato chips, candy bars, or cookies. Beginning Monday students will be able to buy apples, oranges, and bananas. In the past these items were included only with hot lunch meals. Now students will be able to enjoy these fruits even if they bring their own lunch.

Why is this good news?

Well, for starters apples, oranges, and bananas taste great. Anyone who would rather have a candy bar than an apple must be crazy. If taste alone is not enough to convince you, just think about the facts. Apples are a great source of fiber and vitamin C. Fiber is important because it helps your body to digest food. Vitamin C is needed to keep your bones, teeth, gums, and muscles healthy. Vitamin C can also help protect the body from diseases. Remember, an apple a day keeps the doctor away.

If you do not care much for apples, then try an orange or a banana. Oranges contain more vitamin C than apples. Eating an orange is also a great way to provide calcium for your teeth and bones. As your body ages, calcium helps to make new bone to replace the old worn-out bone. Besides, eating oranges is fun. You can squeeze the juice from the orange into your mouth. Sure, it's messy—but it's also healthy. Eating an orange is one time that you will have a good excuse for making a mess.

If oranges are not for you, there are still bananas. Some people believe that a banana contains everything a body needs. Bananas contain fiber, vitamin C, and potassium. Potassium is very important to your nervous system. It can also help to lower blood pressure. If monkeys love them so should you. So, grab yourself a banana!

As you can see fruits are very healthy. So put down those potato chips and pick up an apple. Put away that candy bar and look for an orange. Trade in that cookie for a ripe banana. You'll be glad you did. Starting Monday you will not need to look any farther than the cafeteria to find yourself a healthy snack.

Modeled Instruction

Directions: Below is an example of a question that can be answered by distinguishing fact from opinion in the passage. Follow the strategy that is explained to help choose the correct answer.

---

1 Which statement from the passage is a fact?

Ⓐ "apples, oranges, and bananas taste great"

Ⓑ "an apple a day keeps the doctor away"

Ⓒ "bananas contain fiber"

Ⓓ "eating oranges is fun"

Strategy: To tell if a statement is a fact or an opinion, think about what you can prove. Statements that can be proven are facts. If a statement cannot be proven it is an opinion. Use the information in the passage to help determine which statements are facts and which are opinions.

U s e   t h i s   s t r a t e g y   t o   d e c i d e   w h i c h   a n s w e r   i s   c o r r e c t.

 Ⓐ "apples, oranges, and bananas taste great"

One person may think that apples, oranges, and bananas taste great. Another person may not like the way these fruits taste. Since you cannot prove that apples, oranges, and bananas taste great, *choice "A" cannot be correct.*

 Ⓒ "bananas contain fiber"

If you were to examine a banana in a lab you could prove that it contains fiber. Since you can prove this, it must be a fact. Therefore, *choice "C" must be the correct answer.*

 Ⓑ "an apple a day keeps the doctor away"

Apples are healthy. This is something that you can prove. However, you cannot prove that eating an apple a day will keep you from having to go to see a doctor. Therefore, *choice "B" cannot be correct.*

 Ⓓ "eating oranges is fun"

This statement is an opinion. Some may find eating oranges to be fun, but others may not. Since this statement is not a fact, *choice "D" cannot be correct.*

Guided Instruction

Directions: Use the hints provided to answer the questions below. For question 2, you must choose the correct answer. For question 3, you will need to write out your answer.

2 **Which sentence from the passage states an opinion?**

Ⓐ "If monkeys love them so should you."

Ⓑ "Oranges contain more vitamin C than apples."

Ⓒ "Some people believe that a banana contains everything a body needs."

Ⓓ "Apples are a great source of fiber and vitamin C."

Hint: Read the answer choices one at a time. To find the statement that is an opinion ask yourself which statement you cannot prove.

3 **Read the following sentence from the passage:**

"Beginning Monday students will be able to buy apples, oranges, and bananas."

Is this statement an example of a fact or an opinion? Explain your answer.

Hint: Think about what makes a statement a fact or an opinion. Ask yourself if the statement tells about something that **is true** or something that someone **believes is true.**

Independent Study

Directions: Answer the following questions on your own. For questions 4, 5, and 6, choose the correct answer. For question 7, you must write out your answer.

4 Which sentence from the passage is NOT a fact?

Ⓐ "Vitamin C can also help protect the body from diseases."

Ⓑ "Anyone who would rather have a candy bar than an apple must be crazy."

Ⓒ "Eating an orange is also a great way to provide calcium for your teeth and bones."

Ⓓ "Fiber is important because it helps your body to digest food."

5 Which sentence from the passage is an opinion?

Ⓐ "Now students will be able to enjoy these fruits even if they bring their own lunch."

Ⓑ "If oranges are not for you, there are still bananas."

Ⓒ "As your body ages, calcium helps to make new bone to replace the old worn-out bone."

Ⓓ "You'll be glad that you did."

6 Which sentence from the passage contains both a fact AND an opinion?

Ⓐ "It can also help to lower your blood pressure."

Ⓑ "Sure, it's messy—but it's also healthy."

Ⓒ "If taste alone is not enough to convince you, just think about the facts."

Ⓓ "In the past these items were only included with lunch meals."

7 Read the following sentence from the passage:

"Besides, eating oranges is fun."

Is this statement an example of a fact or an opinion? Explain your answer.

_____

_____

_____

_____

_____

_____

To predict an outcome means you try to figure out what will happen next or in the future. The answers are not stated in the passage. However, details from the passage can help you to predict outcomes.

Directions: Read the passage below. The passage is followed by questions that can be answered by predicting outcomes. Use this passage to answer all the questions on pages 39–41.

A DAY AT THE BEACH

It was the last day of summer vacation. School would begin tomorrow. Claudine, Sofia, and Dmitri wanted to do something special. Claudine asked Aunt Nora if she would take the three of them to the beach. Aunt Nora helped them get packed. She reminded everyone to bring something to wear on their feet.

"The sand will be very hot," Nora told the children.

Claudine and Dmitri packed sandals to wear on their feet. Sofia did not pack hers. She planned on spending most of the day in the water. She did not think she needed sandals to put on her feet.

After everyone was packed they climbed into the car. The beach was only a few minutes away. On the way to the beach the three children sang songs and laughed. When they arrived at the beach everyone helped to unload the car. Dmitri made sure to bring his bucket. He wanted to find shells for the collection he kept in his room. He planned on placing any shells he found in the bucket.

Sofia carried her towel and a container of cold water. As she walked across the sand she had to keep pouring the cold water on her feet. She could not believe how hot the sand was. She wished that she had listened to Aunt Nora about bringing something to wear on her feet. By the time they all arrived near the ocean there was no more water left in the container that Sofia was carrying.

"That water was supposed to be for us to drink," Dmitri complained to Sofia.

"Don't worry," Aunt Nora told the children "there is a lemonade stand on the boardwalk."

The children quickly ran to the water to play. Aunt Nora sat in her chair to watch them. The sun was shining very brightly. Nora had to hold both hands above her eyes to shade them from the sun. She noticed that all of the other adults on the beach were wearing sunglasses. She wished that she had a pair.

Along the edge of the water Dmitri filled his bucket with shells. It became so heavy that he had to use both hands to carry it. Nearby Claudine and Sofia went for a swim. One boy who was also in the water was floating on a tire tube.

"What a great idea," Sofia exclaimed.

"Next time I will remember to bring one," Claudine added.

The children spent most of the morning swimming in the water. In the afternoon they walked along the edge of the water. Claudine took pictures with her new camera. She used up all of her film.

"These will be great to show my friends in school," Claudine said as she thought about going back to school the next day.

It was hot all day. Aunt Nora took the children to the boardwalk to get some lemonade. They did not care much for lemonade, but at least it was cold. As they walked along the boardwalk they noticed some clouds in the sky. The clouds were very dark. It also became very windy.

"We better pack everything up," Aunt Nora told the children as she looked up at the sky.

Nora and the children walked quickly. They packed everything and returned to the car. Now the sky was very dark.

"Just in time," Nora said as they all got inside the car.

Claudine, Sofia, and Dmitri thanked Aunt Nora for a wonderful day.

Modeled Instruction

Directions: Below is an example of a question that can be answered by using information from the passage to predict an outcome. Follow the strategy that is explained to help choose the correct answer.

1 What will probably happen after Aunt Nora and the children leave the beach? Ⓐ It will begin to snow. Ⓑ It will begin to rain. Ⓒ They will go to a different beach. Ⓓ They will go back to the beach later.

Strategy: Do not look for the answer in the passage. Instead look for details that will help you to make a prediction. Try to find details in the passage that are related in some way to the question. Ask yourself what these details suggest will happen.

Use this strategy to decide which answer is correct.

 Ⓐ It will begin to snow.

Details in the passage explain that it is hot. Also, the first sentence explains that it is the last day of summer vacation. Since it is a hot summer day you would not expect it to snow. Therefore, *choice "A" cannot be correct.*

 Ⓑ It will begin to rain.

Details near the end of the passage explain that the clouds became very dark. Other details state that it was becoming windy and the sky was very dark. These details are describing what you would expect to happen before a rainstorm. Therefore, *choice "B" must be the correct answer.*

 Ⓒ They will go to a different beach.

The details in the passage suggest it is going to rain. If Aunt Nora and the children are leaving the beach because it is about to rain, it does not make sense that they would go to a different beach. It would be raining there as well. Therefore, *choice "C" cannot be correct.*

 Ⓓ They will go back to the beach later.

It would be possible to wait for the rain to end then go back to the beach. However, details in the passage suggest that it is late in the day. Also, in the last line of the passage the children thank Aunt Nora for a wonderful day. This suggests that they do not plan to return to the beach. Therefore, *choice "D" cannot be correct.*

Guided Instruction

Directions: Use the hints provided to answer the questions below. For question 2, you must choose the correct answer. For question 3, you will need to write out your answer.

---

2 The next time the children go to the beach—

Ⓐ Sofia will probably take sandals for her feet

Ⓑ Claudine will not take her sandals

Ⓒ Dmitri will probably take a bigger bucket

Ⓓ Dmitri will not take his bucket

Hint: Look for details in the passage that suggest something each of the children would do differently next time they go to the beach. Do any of the children do or say something to suggest what they might do differently?

---

3 What will Claudine take with her the next time she goes to the beach? Use details from the passage to support your answer.

_____

_____

_____

_____

_____

_____

_____

_____

_____

_____

_____

_____

_____

_____

_____

_____

Hint: Read the parts of the passage that mention Claudine. Think about what she does and what she says. Use these details to help you predict what she will take to the beach next time.

Independent Study

Directions: Answer the following questions on your own. For questions 4, 5, and 6, choose the correct answer. For question 7, you must write out your answer.

4 From the passage you can tell that—

Ⓐ Sofia will buy a camera

Ⓑ Claudine will give Sofia her camera

Ⓒ Claudine will take the pictures she took at the beach to school

Ⓓ Claudine will give the pictures she took at the beach to Aunt Nora

5 What did Dmitri most likely do with the shells he put in the bucket?

Ⓐ threw them into the water

Ⓑ buried them in the sand

Ⓒ left them on the beach

Ⓓ took them home

6 The day after their trip to the beach the children will most likely—

Ⓐ go back to school

Ⓑ go back to the beach

Ⓒ fill the container with lemonade

Ⓓ take more pictures with Claudine's camera

7 What one item will Aunt Nora probably take to the beach next time? Use details from the passage to support your answer.

_____

_____

_____

_____

_____

_____

_____

_____

_____

_____

_____

_____

_____

To draw conclusions you must use the information in the passage plus your own judgment. To answer questions that require you to draw conclusions you must think about what the information in the passage suggests. Conclusions must be based on facts found in the passage.

Directions: Read the passage below. The passage is followed by questions that can be answered by drawing conclusions. Use this passage to answer all the questions on pages 43–45.

Clara Barton

Clara Barton was a shy girl who grew up on a farm. She was born in Massachusetts on December 25, 1821. She was the youngest of five children. Her father had been a soldier and was a respected member of the community. His stories about life as a soldier interested Clara. She felt sorry for soldiers who were hurt in battle.

As a child, Clara would often play nurse. She would take care of sick or injured pets. When she was 11 years old she took care of her brother who was very sick. She took care of him for two years.

Clara was a very educated girl. Growing up in a house with two brothers and two sisters, she learned a lot. From her older brothers and sisters, she learned about geography, spelling, math, and sports. Clara Barton started to go to school when she was four years old.

When Clara was 17 years old she became a teacher. Only six years later she started her own school. Over 600 students attended her school. Instead of hiring Clara to run the school, the school board hired a man. Clara was frustrated. She decided she needed a change in her life.

It was at about this time that the War Between the States began. Clara quickly became involved. She wanted to do what she could to help the soldiers. She learned that many soldiers were badly in need of medical supplies. Clara was able to help gather supplies and bring them to the soldiers. She also cooked food and cared for them. Clara became known as the "Angel of the Battlefield."

After the war was over she was given permission by President Lincoln to begin writing letters to help find missing soldiers. She was often able to determine where these soldiers were and notify their families. She gave up four years of her time and more than $10,000 of her own money for this purpose. The U.S. Congress voted to give her back the money she had spent, but she declined to take it.

By 1869 Clara had become tired and worn down from all of her hard work. Her doctor suggested that she try to slow down for a while. She decided to go to Europe to regain her health. While she was in Europe she became involved with the Red Cross. The Red Cross helped provide relief and supplies for soldiers and people in need. Clara believed that there should be a Red Cross in the United States. When Clara returned to the United States she helped to create the American Red Cross.

Clara Barton was the first president of the Red Cross in America. She reached out to many different people in need—not just soldiers. For 23 years she directed relief efforts. She helped to provide relief for people who suffered because of war, famines, earthquakes, and other disasters. Clara remained president of the Red Cross until 1904. She then returned to her home in Maryland where she lived the remainder of her life.

Clara Barton is remembered for the caring person that she was. Most of her life was spent caring for others. She thought of her life as a mission. This mission could be expressed best by her own words: "You must never so much as think whether you like it or not, whether it is bearable or not; you must never think of anything except the need, and how to meet it."

Modeled Instruction

Directions: Below is an example of a question that can be answered by drawing conclusions about the passage. Follow the strategy that is explained to help choose the correct answer.

---

1 **Why do you think Clara Barton was called "Angel of the Battlefield"?**

Ⓐ because she started the Red Cross

Ⓑ because she took care of soldiers hurt in a war

Ⓒ because she prayed for the soldiers

Ⓓ because she helped families to find missing soldiers

Strategy: Look for details in the passage that help you to draw conclusions. Think about what these details tell you. Ask yourself what you can conclude from the facts you are given.

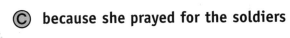
Use this strategy to decide which answer is correct.

 Ⓐ **because she started the Red Cross**

Clara Barton helped to start the American Red Cross. However, this happened after she was already known as the "Angel of the Battlefield." From this you can conclude that *choice "A" cannot be correct.*

Ⓒ **because she prayed for the soldiers**

There is no information in the passage to suggest that Clara Barton prayed for the soldiers. From this you can conclude that *choice "C" cannot be correct.*

 Ⓑ **because she took care of soldiers hurt in a war**

During the War Between the States, Clara Barton spent a great deal of time and effort helping soldiers. It was during this time that people began to call her the "Angel of the Battlefield." From this information you can conclude that *choice "B" is the correct answer.*

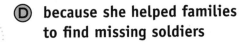 Ⓓ **because she helped families to find missing soldiers**

Following the Civil War, Clara Barton did spend much time helping to find missing soldiers. However, by this time she was already being called the "Angel of the Battlefield." From this you can conclude that *choice "D" cannot be correct.*

Guided Instruction

Directions: Use the hints provided to answer the questions below. For question 2, you must choose the correct answer. For question 3, you will need to write out your answer.

2 **You can conclude that Clara's family was well educated because—**

Ⓐ her parents sent her to the best school in the city

Ⓑ her father taught her everything he knew

Ⓒ she learned so much from her brothers and sisters

Ⓓ she taught herself everything she needed to know

Hint: Find details in the passage that tell about Clara's childhood. Look for facts about the type of education she received. Ask yourself what you can conclude from this information.

3 **Why did Clara Barton become so interested in helping soldiers?**

_____

_____

_____

_____

_____

_____

_____

_____

_____

_____

_____

_____

_____

_____

_____

_____

_____

_____

Hint: Think about how Clara came to learn about soldiers and their needs. Were there any people or events that had an important impact on her? Think about what you can conclude from this information.

Independent Study

Directions: Answer the following questions on your own. For questions 4, 5, and 6, choose the correct answer. For question 7, you must write out your answer.

4 From the passage it can be concluded that Clara didn't rest long in Europe because—

- (A) she wanted to join the Red Cross
- (B) she was worn down and needed some rest
- (C) she no longer wanted to live in the United States
- (D) she was hoping to find soldiers who were missing

5 Why did Clara stop teaching at the school that she opened?

- (A) because there were too many students to teach
- (B) because she wanted to fight in the Civil War along with the soldiers
- (C) because she needed a rest
- (D) because she thought she should have been hired to run the school

6 How did Clara feel about the work of the Red Cross in Europe?

- (A) She thought they were a happy group.
- (B) She thought they didn't have enough people.
- (C) She thought they did very important work.
- (D) She thought they should work in hospitals.

7 How did Clara's childhood help prepare her for the work she did as an adult?

_____

_____

_____

_____

_____

_____

_____

_____

_____

_____

_____

_____

Skill 11: Make Inferences

To answer some questions you must make inferences. An inference is a decision or an opinion that is based upon information that is assumed. It is made from context or visual aids, such as maps or photos. Inferences are not based upon stated facts and are not always correct.

INFORMATION *Ann is ill.*
INFERENCE *She will not go to school tomorrow.*

Directions: Read the passage below. The passage is followed by questions that can be answered by making inferences. Use this passage to answer all the questions on pages 47–49.

Hi Dario,

How is everything? Things are going pretty well for me. It took some time, but I am getting adjusted to my new home. Life in a big city is much different than in a small town. Do you remember how we used to run through the fields and jump into the piles of hay? Well, there aren't many fields or any hay here. But in the winter there is a lot of snow. Playing in the snow can be fun. Maybe someday you can come visit me. I just know that you would enjoy the snow.

Life here is very fast paced. People always seem to walk like they are late for an important meeting. Many of the people do not even take the time to say "hello." I remember how we used to wave to everyone we would see walking through town. They always smiled and said "hello." I really miss that.

There are some good things about living in a big city. The tall buildings are really amazing. Whenever I drive across the bridge I cannot help staring at the beautiful city skyline. There are also a lot of things to do here. There is a baseball team, a football team, a basketball team, and a hockey team if you like sports. There are also many theaters where you can go to see plays and musicals. There are also two libraries near where I live. One of them is just for students. But my favorite part of the city is the art museum. Just last week I saw some really amazing paintings at the museum. Here is a map to show you where all these things are.

I have made many new friends in the past few months. They think my stories about growing up on a farm are really interesting. I don't understand why, but they find it hard to believe that I milked a cow. I keep telling them that I find it hard to believe that they never milked a cow. My friends here are fun to play with and have taught me some great games. One of my favorite games is handball. You must take turns hitting a rubber ball against a brick wall. I guess that's why we never played this game growing up.

How is everyone doing? Is your sister feeling better? Say hello to your mom and dad. Ask your mom if she can send me a box of her homemade cookies. If your family ever decides to move to the city she can open a bakery. There would be plenty of customers. It is much more crowded here. Sometimes my father can't even find a parking space for his car.

Well, I have to go now. Please write back when you get a chance. Maybe this summer you can come visit. If not, I will ask if I can visit you. It would be nice to see the old town again. For some reason, I still think of it as home.

Your Friend, Anna

Modeled Instruction

Directions: Below is an example of a question that can be answered by making inferences about the passage. Follow the strategy that is explained to help choose the correct answer.

---

1 In the city where Anna now lives—

(A) there are more people than in the town where she used to live

(B) people do not like sports

(C) it does not get as cold as the town where she used to live

(D) there are many farms with cows

Strategy: Think about what the details in the letter suggest. You will not be able to find specific facts that tell you the answer. You must look at each answer choice and try to find details to support it. Ask yourself which answer makes the most sense.

Use this strategy to decide which answer is correct.

 (A) **there are more people than in the town where she used to live**

Nowhere in the letter does it actually say that there are more people in the city. However, there are details that do suggest this. You can infer that there are NOT many people in the town where she used to live because she refers to it as a "small town." Therefore, *choice "A" would be the best answer to this question.*

 (B) **people do not like sports**

In the third paragraph of the letter Anna talks about the different teams that play sports in the city. From this you can infer that many people who live in the city enjoy sports. Therefore, *choice "B" cannot be correct.*

 (C) **it does not get as cold as the town where she used to live**

In the first paragraph of the letter Anna mentions that it snows in the city where she lives. From this you can infer that it gets cold in the city where she now lives. The passage also suggests that it does not get very cold in the town where Anna used to live. Therefore, *choice "C" cannot be correct.*

 (D) **there are many farms with cows**

In the letter, Anna states that there aren't many fields in the city. She also tells Dario that her new friends can't believe that she has milked a cow before. From this you can infer there aren't any farms with cows where Anna now lives. Therefore, *choice "D" cannot be correct.*

Guided Instruction

Directions: Use the hints provided to answer the questions below. For question 2, you must choose the correct answer. For question 3, you will need to write out your answer.

---

2   **Which of the following describes how Anna probably feels about living in a big city?**

   Ⓐ She loves living in a big city.

   Ⓑ She does not like living in a big city.

   Ⓒ She likes living in a big city, but not as much as where she used to live.

   Ⓓ She likes living in a big city even more than where she used to live.

Hint: Think about how Anna describes life in a big city. Compare this to how she talks about the old town where she used to live. What can you infer from this information?

---

3   **Areas of a city are often named for buildings that are there or by events that happen there. For example, the area near the museums might be called the Museum District. Name two other areas of Anna's city and explain why you gave them that name.**

Hint: Look at the different places in Anna's city. Think about why you would go to each of them and what you would call them.

_____

_____

_____

_____

_____

_____

_____

_____

_____

_____

Independent Study

Directions: Answer the following questions on your own. For questions 4, 5, and 6, choose the correct answer. For question 7, you must write out your answer.

4 From the letter you can tell—

  (A) Anna would like to live in the city for the rest of her life

  (B) Anna probably has not seen Dario since she moved to the city

  (C) Dario plans on moving to the city in the future

  (D) Dario has probably been to the city at some point in his life

5 Why do you think Anna and Dario never played handball together?

  (A) They did not like the game.

  (B) The game was not allowed in the town where they lived.

  (C) There were not many buildings with brick walls in the town where they lived.

  (D) The buildings in the town where they lived were too close to each other.

6 What do you think Anna's new address is?

  (A) 213 Third Ave.

  (B) 124 23rd St.

  (C) 317 First Ave.

  (D) 215 26th St.

7 Why do think that Anna's new friends find her stories about growing up on a farm so interesting?

_____

_____

_____

_____

_____

_____

_____

_____

_____

_____

_____

_____

_____

Skill 12: Analyze Point of View and Purpose

To analyze a point of view or the purpose in a passage, you need to try to put yourself in the place of the author.

POINT OF VIEW	what the author believes about a topic
PURPOSE	why the author wrote the passage

Directions: Read the letter below. The letter is followed by questions that can be answered by analyzing the author's point of view and purpose. Use this letter to answer all the questions on pages 51–53.

The Truth about Sharks

Some people say sharks are monsters. There have even been books, movies, and television shows that tell stories about sharks causing terror. But these stories and many of our beliefs about sharks could not be further from the truth.

Sharks are great hunters and large sharks are certainly able to cause harm. But most sharks are not as dangerous as people think. The truth is that sharks attack about 100 people each year. But this is far less than the number of people attacked by dogs. It is even less than the number of people attacked by elephants. There are more than 350 types of sharks. But only 32 of them have been known to attack people. Your chances of being struck by lightning are 30 times greater than your chances of being attacked by a shark. In fact, bees, wasps, and snakes are responsible for more human deaths than sharks. When sharks do attack a person it is usually a case of mistaken identity. A shark may think that the person is a large fish or a sea lion.

Many people think sharks swim through the water and never stop eating. This is not true at all. Sharks actually eat very little compared to other animals in the water. Most sharks eat only about 2% of their body weight each day. Dolphins will sometimes eat more than 5% of their body weight. Yet, no one thinks of a dolphin as being a monster. So why do so many people think of sharks as monsters?

Part of the reason people think of sharks as monsters is because of what we see on television and in the movies. It is true that sharks are great hunters capable of causing harm. This is probably another reason why many people fear them. A shark's hunting skills are truly amazing. Some sharks can smell one drop of blood in over 2,000 gallons of water. Sharks can also detect electrical impulses from other animals in the ocean. This means they can hunt for food without seeing or smelling. Once a shark finds its meal it can use its teeth. Most sharks have rows of razor sharp teeth. Since sharks bite down with a great amount of force they lose many teeth when feeding. Some sharks lose over 30,000 teeth in a lifetime. But because they have rows of teeth, a new tooth can quickly replace one that has fallen out. However, not all sharks use their teeth. The basking shark uses its gills to help filter small particles of food, called plankton, from the water. The whale shark, which is the largest type of shark, also eats in a similar way.

Although much has been learned about sharks in recent years, we still do not know all that we would like to. For example, we do not have a very good idea about how fast they grow or how long they can live. The fact that there is still much we do not know is probably another reason why some people think of them as monsters. People are often afraid of things they do not understand or know little about.

Try to learn more about these great fish. There are so many places to go to get an up-close look at sharks. Why not visit the local aquarium? You could learn all kinds of facts from people who know these sharks best. You may even be able to find a few good books about this misunderstood animal. The more time you take to learn about sharks the more you will begin to see that they are not such monsters after all.

Modeled Instruction

Directions: Below is an example of a question that can be answered by analyzing the author's point of view and purpose. Follow the strategy that is explained to help choose the correct answer.

> **1 The author of this essay probably believes that—**
>
> Ⓐ people watch too much television
>
> Ⓑ there are no good books about sharks
>
> Ⓒ people should learn more about sharks
>
> Ⓓ sharks cannot hurt people

Strategy: Think about the entire passage, not just a section of it. In order to understand an author's point of view or purpose you must consider all of the information that is given. If you only focus on a few details you may get the wrong idea about what the author believes or is trying to say.

Use this strategy to decide which answer is correct.

 Ⓐ people watch too much television

In part of the essay the author does suggest that people probably get the wrong idea about sharks from some television shows. However, when reading the entire essay there is no information that states people watch too much television. Therefore, *choice "A" cannot be correct.*

 Ⓒ people should learn more about sharks

In the first half of the essay the author explains that many people have the wrong ideas about sharks. In the last two paragraphs the author talks about how there is much to learn about sharks and suggests ways to learn about them. This suggests that the author believes people should learn more about sharks. Therefore, *choice "C" is the correct answer.*

 Ⓑ there are no good books about sharks

In the first paragraph the author states that some books tell stories about sharks that "could not be further from the truth." However, in the last paragraph the author suggests that there are some good books about sharks. Therefore, *choice "B" cannot be correct.*

Ⓓ sharks cannot hurt people

The author does state that sharks are not as dangerous as people think. However, the author also states that they are capable of causing harm. Also, the author does include details in the passage about people being attacked by sharks. Therefore, *choice "D" cannot be correct.*

Guided Instruction

Directions: Use the hints provided to answer the questions below. For question 2, you must choose the correct answer. For question 3, you will need to write out your answer.

2 **With which of the following statements would the author of this essay be most likely to agree?**

(A) The more you understand about something, the less likely you are to be afraid of it.

(B) The less you know about something, the less there is for you to be afraid of.

(C) Sharks will only hurt people who show they are afraid.

(D) People should be afraid of dolphins and elephants.

Hint: Consider each answer choice. Look for details in the essay to support each possible answer. Which choice is *best* supported by the details you can find?

3 **What does the author believe is the *best* way for people to overcome their fear of sharks?**

_____

_____

_____

_____

_____

_____

_____

_____

_____

_____

_____

_____

_____

_____

_____

_____

Hint: Think about things from the author's point of view. Why does the author believe that people fear sharks? What suggestion provided by the author could help someone to overcome this fear?

Independent Study

Directions: Answer the following questions on your own. For questions 4, 5, and 6, choose the correct answer. For question 7, you must write out your answer.

4 The author's main purpose for writing this essay is to—

Ⓐ help the reader to better understand sharks

Ⓑ inform the reader how to find out more about sharks

Ⓒ tell an entertaining story about sharks

Ⓓ explain why sharks are great hunters

6 Which of the following does the author believe to be true?

Ⓐ No sharks are safe to swim with.

Ⓑ All sharks are safe to swim with.

Ⓒ Only people who work at aquariums know the true facts about sharks.

Ⓓ Most people do not know the true facts about sharks.

5 Which point of view is NOT expressed by the author in the essay?

Ⓐ Snakes should be considered more dangerous than sharks.

Ⓑ There are no such things as monsters.

Ⓒ There is still much to be learned about sharks.

Ⓓ You can't always believe what you see on television or in the movies.

7 Give two reasons why the author believes people think of sharks as monsters.

_____

_____

_____

_____

_____

_____

_____

_____

_____

_____

_____

_____

_____

_____

Skill 13: Identify Literary Forms and Sources of Information

To answer some questions you must be able to identify different types of passages. For example, you must know the difference between a poem and a story. Also, some questions will ask you to tell where you are likely to find different types of information. For example, information about current events might be found in a newspaper.

Directions: Read the passage below. The passage is followed by questions that can be answered by identifying literary forms and sources of information. Use this passage to answer all the questions on pages 55–57.

Jessica's Guitar

Jessica had played a lot of different instruments. Her problem was that she had not played many of them for very long. She had played the clarinet. She did not like the clarinet because she did not like its feel. Jessica did not like all the buttons and having to blow into the instrument. She had played violin. Jessica did not like the violin because holding the instrument on her shoulder was uncomfortable. Her parents had told her that she should stick with one instrument. Still, Jessica had quit playing both.

Jessica knew it would be hard to convince her parents to let her play guitar. She liked the guitar because it was much more a part of the music she liked than the other instruments. All of her favorite songs involved the guitar. Jessica told her parents she wanted to play guitar. They asked her why she would not quit the guitar as she had with the other instruments. Jessica had no answer.

Jessica had to figure out a way to convince her parents to let her play guitar. The next day at school, she went to the library. She decided to discover more about the guitar. She was intrigued at what she found. Jessica found out many facts about the guitar. She learned that the modern guitar was invented in Spain. In the early 1800s, a man named Antonio de Torres Jurado created the first version of the six-string instrument we know today. When it was first invented, the guitar was not very popular. The guitar was not used a lot until the middle of the 1900s in the United States. A man named Les Paul perfected the electric guitar in the 1940s. Ten years later, rock 'n' roll became popular and the guitar became one of the most well-known instruments. The history of the guitar fascinated Jessica.

Jessica did not know if her new knowledge would convince her parents to allow her to learn to play the guitar. She told them all she had learned that night. Her parents told her that she would still have to practice the guitar. They told her it would be difficult to play just like the other instruments. The next day, Jessica got her first guitar.

Modeled Instruction

Directions: Below is an example of a question that can be answered by identifying literary forms and sources of information. Follow the strategy that is explained to help choose the correct answer.

---

1 This passage is an example of—

Ⓐ a story

Ⓑ a poem

Ⓒ a biography

Ⓓ an essay

Strategy: Think about the following:

- What can you tell about the style in which the passage was written?

- What type of information can be found in the passage?

- Why might you choose to read the passage?

Asking yourself these three questions will help you to choose the correct answer.

Use this strategy to decide which answer is correct.

 Ⓐ **a story**

A story can tell about people and events. Some stories are true and some are made up. The purpose of a story is to entertain. All of these accurately describe the passage. Based on this information, *choice "A" is correct.*

 Ⓒ **a biography**

A biography tells about the life of a person. Usually biographies are about famous or well-known people. Although the passage is about Jessica, it does not tell about her entire life. Therefore, *choice "C" cannot be the answer.*

 Ⓑ **a poem**

In poems words are arranged in patterns. Sometimes words in poems rhyme and sometimes the words can be spoken in rhythm. Since this does NOT describe the passage, *choice "B" cannot be the answer.*

 Ⓓ **an essay**

An essay is usually written about one topic or idea. It provides information that expresses the author's point of view. Since the main purpose of the passage is NOT to give information or express a point of view, *choice "D" cannot be the correct answer.*

Guided Instruction

Directions: Use the hints provided to answer the questions below. For question 2, you must choose the correct answer. For question 3, you will need to write out your answer.

2 The purpose of this passage is to—

(A) inform

(B) entertain

(C) teach a lesson

(D) talk someone into something

Hint: Describe the passage to yourself. Think about why the passage was probably written. Why might someone choose to read this passage?

3 Explain how you can tell that this passage is NOT an example of a myth.

_____

_____

_____

_____

_____

_____

_____

_____

_____

_____

_____

_____

_____

_____

_____

_____

_____

Hint: A myth is a story about heroes, imaginary creatures, or gods. It is often used to explain the customs or beliefs of a group of people. Think about how this description of a myth compares to the passage you read.

Independent Study

Directions: Answer the following questions on your own. For questions 4, 5, and 6, choose the correct answer. For question 7, you must write out your answer.

4 **The books that Jessica read to learn about the guitar were most likely written to—**

Ⓐ inform

Ⓑ entertain

Ⓒ teach a lesson

Ⓓ talk someone into something

5 **What should Jessica read if she wants to learn more about the life of the person who perfected the electric guitar?**

Ⓐ a book about the history of the guitar

Ⓑ a letter written by Les Paul

Ⓒ a myth about the first guitar

Ⓓ a biography of Les Paul

6 **Where would you most likely find this passage?**

Ⓐ in a book containing a collection of folk tales

Ⓑ in the art section of a newspaper

Ⓒ in a book containing a collection of short stories

Ⓓ in a magazine for guitar collectors

7 **How would this passage be different if it were written as a play?**

_____

_____

_____

_____

_____

_____

_____

_____

_____

_____

_____

_____

_____

_____

_____

Skill 14: Apply Prior Knowledge

Apply prior knowledge means that you must use what you already know to help answer a question. The passage will contain information that will be helpful to you. However, you must use this information together with knowledge you already have.

Directions: Read the passage below. The passage is followed by questions that can be answered by applying prior knowledge. Use this passage to answer all the questions on pages 59–61.

GETTING AROUND

Walk down the street and you will probably see a car pass you by. Look up in the sky and you will see a plane. If you live near the water you might see a boat. And if you live near the railroad you might see a train. There are so many ways to get from one place to the next. What is really amazing is how quickly the way people travel has changed. Just think—in less than 100 years people have gone from traveling by horse and carriage to traveling to the moon by rocket.

Looking back over time there have been many changes in the way people travel. One of the most popular forms of travel in the 1800s was the horse and carriage. People could travel over dirt roads in a carriage pulled by a team of horses. Sometimes they would travel great distances. However, traveling this way took a great deal of time. A faster way to travel was by train. Trains powered by steam engines could travel about 10 miles in one hour. They could also carry a large number of people. As more and more railroads were built, travel by train became very popular. In the United States, over 160,000 miles of track were built by 1880. The railroad tracks connected cities and crossed mountains. People could travel across the country more quickly than ever before.

The steamboat was another way of traveling. In the early 1800s people used steamboats to travel across water. Early steamboats could travel five miles in one hour. Before railroads became so widespread, steamboats were the best way to travel great distances. However, they were limited to travel along waterways.

In the late 1800s and early 1900s things changed quickly. One of the most important changes in travel took place. Cars rapidly became a popular way to travel. At first they were very expensive. Many people could not afford to buy them. But as cars became less expensive they began to gain popularity. Soon paved roads were being built everywhere. Today you can travel by car across an entire continent.

At about the same time cars began to catch on, a new way of travel was introduced. In 1903 the Wright brothers invented and flew an engine-powered plane. The first airplanes were very dangerous to fly. It took many years before travel by plane was considered safe. By 1950 planes had become much safer and more comfortable. Jet-powered planes made it possible to travel farther and faster.

It is hard to believe that less than 20 years later a man could travel to the moon in a rocket. But that's just what happened. In 1969 a rocket carrying four men traveled to the moon. Several more rockets have made the trip since then. More recently, space shuttles have been used to travel into outer space. What will be next?

The way people travel continues to change. More then ever people travel all around the world. They are able to get from one place to another quicker than ever. Not so long ago people only thought about traveling cross-country. Today people can travel to the stars.

Modeled Instruction

Directions: Below is an example of a question that can be answered by applying prior knowledge. Follow the strategy that is explained to help choose the correct answer.

1 **Which would be the best way to travel from New York to California if you wanted to get there as quickly as possible?**

Ⓐ space shuttle

Ⓑ car

Ⓒ steamboat

Ⓓ airplane

Strategy: First look for information in the passage that can be used to help answer the question. Then think about what you already know. What you already know should help you to better understand the information in the passage. Choose the answer that makes the most sense to you.

Use this strategy to decide which answer is correct.

 Ⓐ space shuttle

From the passage you know that space shuttles travel into outer space. To do this they must travel very fast. However, you should already know that people do not use space shuttles to travel across the country. Therefore, *choice "A" cannot be the answer.*

 Ⓒ steamboat

From the passage you know that steamboats could be used to travel great distances along waterways. However, you should already know that to travel from New York to California it is necessary to cross over land. Therefore, *choice "C" cannot be the answer.*

 Ⓑ car

From the passage you know that it is possible to travel across an entire continent by car. However, you should already know that it would take a long time to drive from New York to California. Therefore, *choice "B" cannot be the answer.*

 Ⓓ airplane

From the passage you know that airplanes are used to travel great distances at a fast speed. Also, you should already know that people often fly to different places around the world. Many people do fly from New York to California. Therefore you can conclude that *choice "D" is the best possible answer.*

Guided Instruction

Directions: Use the hints provided to answer the questions below. For question 2, you must choose the correct answer. For question 3, you will need to write out your answer.

---

2 **When is it better to travel by car than by airplane?**

Ⓐ when you must travel to a place that is close to where you are

Ⓑ when you have to travel a great distance in a short amount of time

Ⓒ when you need to cross over a large body of water

Ⓓ when you have to travel with a large group of people

Hint: Think about the advantages of traveling by car. You will find some details in the passage. But remember to consider what you already know about cars and airplanes before choosing an answer.

---

3 **How are traveling by train and traveling by bus alike?**

_____

_____

_____

_____

_____

_____

_____

_____

_____

_____

_____

_____

_____

_____

_____

Hint: The passage provides details about traveling by train. However, it does not mention anything about buses. You will need to think about what you already know about traveling by bus.

Independent Study

Directions: Answer the following questions on your own. For questions 4, 5, and 6, choose the correct answer. For question 7, you must write out your answer.

---

4 **Which of the following was probably replaced by the car?**

Ⓐ airplane

Ⓑ horse and carriage

Ⓒ steamboat

Ⓓ steam-engine train

---

6 **Today a large group of people would most likely travel by—**

Ⓐ rocket

Ⓑ car

Ⓒ horse and carriage

Ⓓ airplane

---

5 **Why might someone want to travel by horse and carriage in the 1800s?**

Ⓐ They need to go someplace that is far away.

Ⓑ They need to travel through deep water.

Ⓒ They need to travel where there are no paved roads.

Ⓓ They need to get somewhere as quickly as possible.

---

7 **If you were planning a trip to a place halfway around the world how would you travel to get there? Explain the reasons for your choice.**

_____

_____

_____

_____

_____

_____

_____

_____

_____

_____

_____

_____

_____

_____

_____

PART B

The 14 Essential Skills for Reading Success

All Together

Section 1:
Modeled Instruction and Guided Instruction

Each of the fourteen reading comprehension skills are taught all together in this part. Part B is divided into two sections.

Section 1: Modeled Instruction and Guided Instruction

In this section, you will read a passage and answer fourteen questions. The questions will be both multiple-choice and open-ended. Each question covers one of the fourteen essential skills. There will be a *Reminder* to help you remember the strategy needed to answer each question.

Section 2: Independent Study

This section is made up of two themes. Each theme has four passages with fourteen essential skill questions. You are on your own to answer them. There will be different types of passages: stories, biographies, poems, fact-filled material, notes, timelines, letters, and other types of writings. At the end of each theme, there will be three questions about how the passages are connected to their theme. The two themes are:

Theme A: *Government by the People and for the People*

Theme B: *The Attraction of Outer Space*

The passage in this section is followed by fourteen questions. Each question has a reminder to help you recall which skill you must rely on to answer the question correctly.

Directions: Read the passage below and answer the questions that follow. Use the reminders provided to help you recall the correct strategy for answering each type of question.

Francine's Great Day

The car door flew open and Francine raced up the steps leading to the front door. She could not wait to see Grandma again. It had been almost three months since the last time Francine and her family came for a visit.

Just as Francine was about to press the button to ring the bell, the front door opened. There Grandma stood, waiting for her with open arms. Francine and Grandma shared a warm *embrace* as the rest of the family made their way up the steps leading to the front door.

"Come, everyone, come," Grandma cheered with a smile. She greeted Francine's younger brother, Giorgio, with a kiss on both cheeks and gave Mama and Papa each a big hug.

"What's for dinner?" Francine asked, unable to wait until everyone was inside. "I hope you made some of your 'world famous' lasagna and meatballs."

Before Grandma had a chance to reply, Francine could smell the gravy that had greeted her so many times before when she and her family came to visit. Francine's mother used the same recipe, but no one could make gravy quite like Grandma—just the right amount of parsley and oregano.

"I knew you would make lasagna and meatballs, I just knew it," Francine declared.

"Come, Grandpa is waiting," Grandma urged as she led everyone into the dining room.

Mama, Papa, Giorgio, and Francine interrupted Grandpa while he was placing silverware on the table. They each gave him a hug and a kiss on both cheeks. Then they all helped finish setting the table.

Francine asked Grandpa if he would play a game of chess with her after dinner. Grandpa agreed. She loved playing chess, especially with Grandpa. She liked the fact that he would never just let her win. Francine could tell some adults would let her win because she was only nine-years old. Even though she never beat Grandpa at chess, she would have fun every time.

Francine knew she would have to try her best if she were to beat Grandpa.

As was Grandma's tradition on Sunday, dinner was served promptly at 1 P.M. Francine ate two meatballs with her lasagna and was ready for a second serving. She held out her plate and asked her mother if she could have some more.

"Save some room for the ice cream," Mama reminded Francine.

Grandma would always make ice cream by herself using the best ingredients. It was a lot of hard work, but it tasted so much better than the kind you could get from the store.

After dinner, Grandma gave Francine and Giorgio each one scoop of ice cream with chocolate sprinkles. Francine ate her ice cream slowly, making sure to enjoy each spoonful. Giorgio, however, preferred to devour his as quickly as possible. When he was done he looked up at Grandma with a big vanilla ice cream smile.

"Ready for that game of chess?" Grandpa asked.

Francine raced to the chessboard and began setting up all of the pieces. Once the pieces were all set in place, Grandpa pulled up a chair. He looked up at Francine and whispered, "I can't decide."

"Can't decide what?" Francine asked.

"I can't decide which I enjoy more—Grandma's lasagna or playing chess with you," Grandpa chuckled.

The two spent the rest of the afternoon playing chess. Francine had a smile on her face the entire time. She thought to herself how much she loved Grandma's lasagna, but was certain that she enjoyed chess with Grandpa even more.

Directions: Answer the following questions using the reminders provided to help you recall the correct strategy for answering each type of question.

Recall Facts and Details

> **1 How old is Francine?**
>
> (A) 8 years old
>
> (B) 9 years old
>
> (C) 10 years old
>
> (D) You cannot tell from reading the passage.

Reminder: The answer to this question can be found right in the passage. Look for key words. Read the sentences with these key words very carefully to find the detail or fact needed to answer the question correctly.

Identify Main Idea

> **2 What would be another good title for this story?**
>
> (A) "Lasagna and Ice Cream"
>
> (B) "A Day with Grandma and Grandpa"
>
> (C) "The Chess Game"
>
> (D) "Grandma and Grandpa Come for a Visit"

Reminder: The main idea is what the whole story is about. To answer this question correctly you need to think about the entire passage, not just one part.

Identify Sequence

3 What does Francine do after she eats her ice cream?

Ⓐ She gives her Grandpa a hug and a kiss.

Ⓑ She helps clean off the table.

Ⓒ She asks "What's for dinner?"

Ⓓ She plays chess with Grandpa.

✺ **Reminder:** Find each of the answer choices within the passage. Make a timeline to help you choose the correct answer.

Analyze Language and Vocabulary

4 Another word for *embrace* is—

Ⓐ tangled

Ⓑ together

Ⓒ handshake

Ⓓ hug

✺ **Reminder:** This type of question asks you to identify the meaning of a word. To find the meaning of a word you must think about how the word is used in the passage.

Analyze Character, Plot, and Setting

5 You can tell from reading the story that Grandma is—

Ⓐ kind

Ⓑ grumpy

Ⓒ funny

Ⓓ quiet

✺ **Reminder:** Describe the character being asked about in the question. Be sure to think about the whole story and select the answer that *best* describes the character.

Recognize Cause and Effect

6 Grandma's ice cream tastes so good because—

Ⓐ she makes it herself using the best ingredients

Ⓑ she serves it right after dinner

Ⓒ she purchases it from the best store in town

Ⓓ she makes sure everyone eats it slowly to enjoy each spoonful

✺ **Reminder:** Cause and effect go together. To answer this type of question you must find the event or action in the answer choice that goes with the event or action in the question.

Compare and Contrast

7 **How does Francine think playing chess with Grandpa is different from playing with other adults?**

_____

_____

_____

_____

_____

_____

_____

_____

_____

_____

_____

_____

_____

_____

_____

_____

_____

_____

Reminder: Compare questions ask you to tell how things are alike. Contrast questions ask you to tell how things are different. Make a chart or a Venn Diagram. Use details from the passage to support your answer.

Distinguish Fact from Opinion

8 **Which of the following is an opinion?**

Ⓐ Grandma always made her own ice cream.

Ⓑ Grandma served dinner promptly at 1 P.M.

Ⓒ Grandma's ice cream is better than the kind you buy in the store.

Ⓓ Francine hoped that Grandma made her "world famous" lasagna.

Reminder: To answer this question you must be able to identify which answer choices are facts and which one is an opinion. Facts can be proven true, opinions cannot.

Predict Outcomes

9 Which of the following will most likely happen the next time Francine visits her grandparents?

Ⓐ She will not want to eat lasagna again.

Ⓑ She will want to play chess with Grandpa again.

Ⓒ She will bring ice cream for dessert.

Ⓓ She will not have as much fun.

Reminder: To predict an outcome you must use information in the story to decide what you think will happen next. More than one answer may seem possible. You must choose the *best* answer.

Draw Conclusions

10 You can tell from reading this story that Francine—

Ⓐ enjoys going on trips with her parents

Ⓑ usually does not have so much fun

Ⓒ has more fun than her brother Giorgio

Ⓓ will be sad when she has to leave

Reminder: To draw conclusions you must think about many different facts and details found in the passage. The passage does not tell you the answer, but it does give you the information you need to draw a conclusion.

Make Inferences

11 Francine's mother got her lasagna and meatballs recipe from—

Ⓐ a friend

Ⓑ a cookbook

Ⓒ Grandma

Ⓓ Grandpa

Reminder: Facts and details in a passage can suggest an answer without actually stating the answer. These questions are asking you to infer the meaning of events or details.

Analyze Point of View and Purpose

12 By writing this passage the author is trying to show—

Ⓐ how different everyone's family is

Ⓑ that all families are the same

Ⓒ that chess is a fun game

Ⓓ how visiting family can be fun

Reminder: How the author feels about a topic is a point of view. Why the author wrote a passage is his or her purpose. Details in a passage often suggest a point of view or purpose.

Identify Literary Forms and Sources of Information

13 **This passage is an example of which of the following?**

Ⓐ fiction

Ⓑ nonfiction

Ⓒ legend

Ⓓ biography

Reminder: Literary form refers to the different styles or types of writing such as stories, nonfiction, biographies, and poems. You can identify each literary form, or genre, by its features.

Apply Prior Knowledge

14 **Why do you think Francine enjoys playing chess with Grandpa even more than eating Grandma's lasagna?**

_____

_____

Reminder: The answer to this question cannot be found in the passage alone. In addition to details from the passage, you must use your own knowledge to help answer the question.

_____

_____

_____

_____

_____

_____

_____

_____

_____

_____

_____

_____

_____

_____

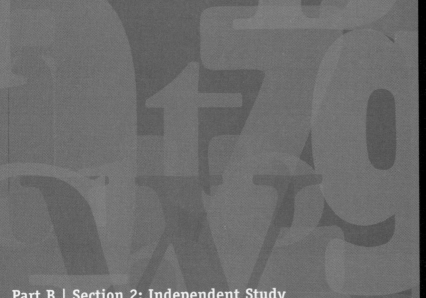

PART B

The 14 Essential Skills for Reading Success

All Together

Section 2: Independent Study

Theme A

Government by the People and for the People

Theme B

The Attraction of Outer Space

Part B | Section 2: Independent Study

This section is made up of two themes. Each theme has four passages with fourteen essential skill questions. You are on your own to answer them. There are different types of passages: stories, biographies, poems, fact-filled material, notes, timelines, letters, and other types of writings. At the end of each theme, there will be three questions about how the passages are connected to their theme. The two themes are:

Theme A: *Government by the People and for the People*
    Selection 1: *Thurgood Marshall*
    Selection 2: *The Field Trip*
    Selection 3: *The Three Branches of the Government*
    Selection 4: *The Flag Goes By*

Theme B: *The Attraction of Outer Space*
    Selection 1: *Neptune: The Eighth Planet*
    Selection 2: *Jacob's Journey*
    Selection 3: *Space Exploration Timeline: 1957–1998*
    Selection 4: *A Letter to an Alien*

Section 2: Independent Study

There are two groups of passages in this Section. Each group is made up of four passages. The four passages are thematically linked. They are written about a single theme. This is the first theme.

Theme A: Government by the People and for the People

Selection 1 | **Directions:** Read the passage below and answer the questions that follow.

Thurgood Marshall

Thurgood Marshall was the first African-American to become a member of the United States Supreme Court. While on the Supreme Court he fought to protect the rights of people. He is considered by many to be a very important person in American history.

Thurgood Marshall was born on July 2, 1908 He grew up in Baltimore, Maryland. He lived with his mother, father, and older brother. His mother was a teacher. His father worked at a railroad.

As a child, Thurgood often got into trouble at school. As punishment his high school teacher would have him read the United States Constitution. When Thurgood graduated from high school he was able to *recite* most of the Constitution from memory.

Near the house where Thurgood and his family lived was a police station. Sometimes Thurgood would see people being arrested. His father would take him to court to watch the trials. Thurgood thought that some people were not treated fairly. He soon became interested in learning about law. However, his mother wanted him to become a dentist.

Thurgood Marshall, circa 1935

Thurgood Marshall graduated from high school at the age of sixteen. He then studied to become a dentist, but he later decided to attend law school. He felt that law was a more important profession. He first went to Lincoln University in Pennsylvania. Later he went to Howard University Law School. He graduated from both with honors.

Marshall spent the next 34 years of his life defending people's rights. He took great pride in helping people who were not treated fairly. He won most of the cases he worked on as a lawyer. In 1961 he became the second African-American to be a member of the United States Circuit Court of Appeals. Six years later he replaced Judge Thomas C. Clark on the United States Supreme Court. He was the first African American to serve on the court. Along with the eight other members of the Supreme Court, Thurgood Marshall made important decisions about legal issues.

Thurgood Marshall was a member of the United States Supreme Court for 24 years. He retired on June 27, 1991. In 1992 the Thurgood Marshall Award was created in his honor. On January 24, 1993 Thurgood Marshall died at the age of 84. Today he is still remembered for his great accomplishments. During his life he helped to bring people together. He helped to make sure that all people were treated fairly by the law.

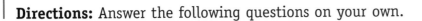

The Thurgood Marshall Lifetime Achievement Award, created for the NAACP Legal Defense and Educational Fund, Inc., Designed by Tina Allen

Directions: Answer the following questions on your own.

1 How many members are on the United States Supreme Court?

Ⓐ one

Ⓑ eight

Ⓒ nine

Ⓓ twelve

2 This passage tells *mostly* about—

Ⓐ the life of Thurgood Marshall

Ⓑ the history of the Supreme Court

Ⓒ how people's rights are protected

Ⓓ how Thurgood Marshall changed the Supreme Court

3 Which of the following happened after Thurgood Marshall attended Lincoln University?

Ⓐ He studied to become a dentist.

Ⓑ He attended Howard University Law School.

Ⓒ His father took him to court to watch trials.

Ⓓ He often got in trouble.

4 You can tell from the third paragraph that the word *recite* means—

Ⓐ to argue

Ⓑ to change

Ⓒ to see clearly

Ⓓ to repeat aloud

5 Which word *best* describes Thurgood Marshall?

Ⓐ shy

Ⓑ lazy

Ⓒ poor

Ⓓ smart

6 Why did Thurgood Marshall read the United States Constitution so much when he was young?

Ⓐ He wanted to learn about law.

Ⓑ It was punishment for getting in trouble at school.

Ⓒ His mother was a teacher.

Ⓓ So that he would be allowed to go to law school.

7 According to the passage how was the Supreme Court different before Thurgood Marshall became a member?

Ⓐ African-Americans were not allowed on the court.

Ⓑ There were no African-American members.

Ⓒ The court did not treat people fairly.

Ⓓ There were only eight members.

8 Which statement from the passage is an example of an opinion?

Ⓐ "Law was a more important profession."

Ⓑ "Thurgood graduated from high school at the age of sixteen."

Ⓒ "He won most the cases he worked on as a lawyer."

Ⓓ "He took great pride in helping people who were not treated fairly."

9 How might things have been different if Thurgood Marshall had taken his mother's advice to become a dentist?

_____

_____

_____

_____

_____

_____

_____

_____

_____

_____

_____

_____

_____

_____

_____

_____

_____

_____

_____

_____

10 Why do you think Thurgood Marshall wanted to go to law school?

Ⓐ He did not want to become a dentist.

Ⓑ He wanted to become a famous person.

Ⓒ He wanted to become the first African-American on the Supreme Court.

Ⓓ He wanted to be able to defend people's rights.

11 How can you tell from the passage that Thurgood Marshall was well-liked?

Ⓐ He graduated law school with honors.

Ⓑ He fought to protect people's rights.

Ⓒ The Thurgood Marshall Award was created in his honor.

Ⓓ He was a member of the United States Supreme Court.

12 The author of the passage probably believes—

Ⓐ Thurgood Marshall was a good lawyer

Ⓑ Thurgood Marshall should have become a dentist

Ⓒ Thurgood Marshall was not given enough credit for the things he did

Ⓓ Thurgood Marshall should not have been punished by his high school teacher

13 Which of the following would be the best place to look for more information about Thurgood Marshall?

Ⓐ a recent newspaper

Ⓑ an encyclopedia

Ⓒ a dictionary

Ⓓ the United States Constitution

14 Thurgood Marshall was admired by many people. Name someone you admire. Tell how this person and Thurgood Marshall are alike.

_____

_____

_____

_____

_____

_____

_____

_____

_____

_____

Selection 2 | **Directions:** Read the passage below and answer the questions that follow.

The Field Trip

Mai could hear her mother calling her from the kitchen. At first she did not want to get out of bed. She was still very tired and wanted to sleep some more. Then, she remembered about the field trip. Her entire class was going to visit the nation's capital in Washington, D.C. Her teacher, Miss Lawrence, planned the trip at the start of the school year. Mai had been waiting patiently for the last six months for this day to arrive.

Mai quickly got dressed and raced to the kitchen. Her breakfast was already on the table. Mai smiled while looking at her mother. "Today is going to be a great day!" Mai declared. She quickly finished her toast and orange juice.

At the school Mai's mother gave her a big hug. "Tell the president I said hello," her mother said as she laughed. Mai gave her mother a kiss. Then she got on the bus along with the rest of the class. On the way to Washington, D.C. she sat next to her best friend Rose. Rose told Mai about the time she took a tour of the White House with her Uncle Roberto. As Mai listened to Rose talk she became more excited. She could not wait to get there.

When the bus arrived at Capitol Hill the class was divided into groups. In each group were one adult and five children. Rose and Mai were in the same group. Miss Lawrence was also part of the group. Mr. Green, a tour guide, walked Mai's group around the area, pointing out all of the buildings and statues.

The first building Mr. Green took the group to see was the Capitol building. This is the building where Congress meets to write the laws of our nation. For almost two hundred years, senators and representatives from all parts of the country have met at this building.

While on Capitol Hill the students were also given a tour of the Library of Congress then Union Station. The Library of Congress was created in 1800 and is the world's largest library. Mai could not believe how big the library was. Mai also enjoyed visiting Union Station. At the time Union Station was opened, in 1908, it was the largest train station in the world. Inside the station are shops, restaurants, and even a movie theater.

After lunch the entire class met at the National Mall. The National Mall is a tree-lined area near Capitol Hill that stretches over two miles long. Miss Lawrence took the class to see the Lincoln Memorial. The 19-foot tall marble statue was built in honor of Abraham Lincoln. Mai also got to see a statue of Thomas Jefferson. This statue was also about 19 feet tall, but was made of bronze. But her favorite sight was the 550-foot tall Washington Monument. The *monument* could be seen from almost anywhere in the city. It was very pretty to look at.

There were two more buildings to see before it was time to go home. First, the class went to see the United States Supreme Court building. This is the place where important legal decisions are made. Mai remembered learning about the Supreme Court in school. One of her heroes was Judge Thurgood Marshall. He was well known for protecting people's rights. Mai thought that when she grew up she would like to become a judge.

The last stop for the day was the White House. Mai and her classmates were given a guided tour of the building. Remembering the message that her mother asked her to deliver, Mai laughed to herself as she kept a look out for the President. As she looked around, Mai thought about all the presidents she had read about in school—Lincoln, Jefferson, Roosevelt, and many others. She was amazed to think that she was standing in the same building where these great presidents also once stood.

After the tour of the White House it was time to go home. When Mai arrived at her house she did not know where to begin. She wanted to tell her mother everything. The two sat down at the kitchen table and shared some milk and cookies. Her mother listened as Mai told her all about the field trip. "Maybe this summer we can take our own field trip to Washington, D.C.," Mai said with a smile. Her mother nodded her head and smiled back.

Directions: Answer the following questions on your own.

1 Where is the National Mall located?

Ⓐ next to Capitol Hill

Ⓑ on Capitol Hill

Ⓒ inside Union Station

Ⓓ above Union Station

2 This passage is *mostly* about—

Ⓐ Mai's trip to the White House

Ⓑ Mai's class trip to the nation's capital

Ⓒ how Mai and Rose had fun together

Ⓓ how Mai decided she wanted to become a judge

3 Which event belongs in the empty box?

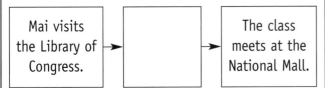

| Mai visits the Library of Congress. | | The class meets at the National Mall. |

Ⓐ Mai and her group went to see Union Station.

Ⓑ Miss Lawrence took the class to see the Lincoln Memorial.

Ⓒ Mr. Green took the group to see the Capitol building.

Ⓓ The class took a tour of the Capitol building.

4 In this passage the word *monument* means—

Ⓐ a small statue of a President

Ⓑ a type of stage or flat surface

Ⓒ a place where people eat lunch

Ⓓ an important building or statue

5 Where does *most* of the story take place?

Ⓐ in Mai's kitchen

Ⓑ at school

Ⓒ Washington D.C.

Ⓓ inside the White House

6 Why did Mai quickly get dressed and race to the kitchen?

Ⓐ She was afraid she would miss her bus.

Ⓑ She was excited about going on the field trip.

Ⓒ Her mother was angry that she was going to be late for school.

Ⓓ Her breakfast was getting cold.

7 Compare and contrast the statues of Abraham Lincoln and Thomas Jefferson. Write about at least one way they are alike and one way they are different.

_____

_____

_____

_____

_____

_____

_____

_____

_____

_____

_____

_____

_____

_____

8 Which statement about the Washington Monument is an opinion?

(A) It is pretty to look at.

(B) It is 550 feet tall.

(C) It was Mai's favorite sight.

(D) It could be seen from almost anywhere in the city.

9 Which of the following will Mai probably do when summer arrives?

(A) go on another field trip with her class

(B) visit the White House with her mother

(C) invite her classmates to stay at her house

(D) visit Miss Lawrence with her mother

10 Why was Mai amazed while standing inside the White House?

(A) It was so big.

(B) It was so pretty.

(C) It was the same place so many great presidents once stood.

(D) It was just like her friend Rose told her it would be.

11 Why did Mai laugh to herself as she kept a look out for the president?

_____

_____

_____

_____

_____

_____

_____

_____

_____

_____

_____

_____

12 The author probably wrote this passage to—

Ⓐ entertain and teach a lesson

Ⓑ inform and entertain

Ⓒ express an opinion

Ⓓ prove a point

13 This passage is an example of—

Ⓐ a biography

Ⓑ a play

Ⓒ a story

Ⓓ an essay

14 The things Mai learns while visiting the Capitol will help her most in which of her classes at school?

Ⓐ History

Ⓑ Geography

Ⓒ Science

Ⓓ Reading

The Three Branches of Government

Aubrey learned about the branches of government today in class.
Below are some of the notes he took.

The Branches of Government

There are three branches of government: Executive, Legislative, and Judicial.

1) EXECUTIVE: This branch of government enforces laws. The president is in charge of the executive branch. The president makes sure that laws are carried out. He or she can also recommend new laws. The president has the power to veto. This means the president will not approve the law. The president is also the commander-in-chief. This means he or she is in charge of the military. The president is elected for a term of four years. A person can only be elected president for two consecutive terms.

2) LEGISLATIVE: This branch of the government makes laws. Congress is the legislative branch of the United States government. All states are represented in Congress. Congress is divided into two parts—the Senate and the House of Representatives. The two parts of Congress work together to propose laws. A law that is proposed is called a bill. Both the Senate and House of Representatives must vote to approve a bill for it to become a law.

Senate: There are two senators from each state. The United States Senate has a total of 100 senators. Senators are elected to a six-year term. Only the Senate can approve or reject treaties and presidential nominations.

House of Representatives: The number of representatives a state has depends on how many people live in the state. States with a large population will have more representatives than states with a small population. There are currently 435 members. Each member is elected to a two-year term. Only the House can create bills about how government money is spent.

3) JUDICIAL: The job of this branch is to interpret laws. Laws are very confusing. Two people may have a different idea about what a law means. The judicial branch looks closely at these laws and interprets what they mean. The United States Supreme Court heads the judicial branch. The judges on the Supreme Court are not elected. The president selects Supreme Court judges. The Senate must approve the judges selected. There is no limit to the number of years a judge can remain on the Supreme Court. The first Supreme Court had only six judges. Today there are nine judges. The judge in charge of the Supreme Court is called the chief justice.

PART B: The 14 Essential Skills for Reading Success — All Together

Separation of Power

The United States government is based on the separation of power. This means each branch has a different role. No one branch has all of the power to govern. All three branches must work together.

– How a Law Is Made –

STEP 1

A bill is introduced in Congress. (A bill may be introduced in the Senate or House of Representatives. Changes to the bill are sometimes made. After changes are made, a vote is taken.)

STEP 2A

If a bill is first approved by the Senate, it must then go to the House of Representatives for a vote.

STEP 2B

If a bill is first approved by the House of Representatives, it must then go to the Senate for a vote.

STEP 3

After a bill is approved by both the House of Representatives and Senate, the bill goes to the president. (The bill becomes a law when the president approves it.)

STEP 4

A law that is passed can be interpreted by the Supreme Court. (If the law is ruled to be unconstitutional it can no longer be a law.)

Checks and Balances

The reason there are three branches of government is to provide a system of checks and balances. This is important so that no one branch of the government has too much power.

Examples of checks and balances–
1) A president may veto a law passed by Congress.
2) Congress can pass a law that has been vetoed with a two-thirds vote. This means two out of every three members of Congress must vote to approve the law.
3) The Supreme Court can declare a law unconstitutional. A law that is ruled unconstitutional can no longer be a law.

Directions: Answer the following questions on your own.

1 **Who can create bills about how money is spent?**

Ⓐ the president

Ⓑ the Senate

Ⓒ the House of Representatives

Ⓓ the Supreme Court

2 **Aubrey uses his notes to make the diagram below.**

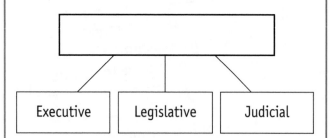

Which title should be placed in the empty box?

Ⓐ "Aubrey's Notes"

Ⓑ "How a Bill Becomes a Law"

Ⓒ "The Senate and the House of Representatives"

Ⓓ "Branches of Government"

3 **Which of the following must happen first for a bill to become a law?**

Ⓐ It must be approved by the president.

Ⓑ It must be approved by the chief justice.

Ⓒ It must be approved by Congress.

Ⓓ It must be approved by the Supreme Court.

4 Explain what the phrase "checks and balances" means. Give one example to show how the government uses checks and balances.

_____

_____

_____

_____

_____

_____

_____

_____

_____

_____

_____

_____

_____

_____

_____

_____

_____

_____

_____

5 Which best describes the role of a member of the executive branch of government?

Ⓐ to make laws

Ⓑ to enforce laws

Ⓒ to interpret laws

Ⓓ to veto laws

6 What happens if the Supreme Court rules that a law is unconstitutional?

Ⓐ It is no longer a law.

Ⓑ It must be vetoed by the president.

Ⓒ A two-thirds vote is needed in Congress to pass the law.

Ⓓ A new law must be made by the Supreme Court.

7 List one way the Senate and House of Representatives are alike and one way they are different.

_____

_____

_____

_____

_____

_____

_____

_____

_____

_____

_____

_____

_____

_____

_____

_____

_____

8 Which of the following is NOT a fact?

(A) There is no limit to the number of years a judge can remain on the Supreme Court.

(B) Laws are very confusing.

(C) The judicial branch looks closely at these laws and interprets what they mean.

(D) The first Supreme Court had only six judges.

9 What will happen if the president vetoes a law that has been passed by Congress?

(A) It will not become a law.

(B) It still becomes a law.

(C) It may not become a law.

(D) It can never become a law.

10 Why are there three branches of government?

   (A) so that laws can be vetoed

   (B) so that each branch can create different laws

   (C) so that no one branch has too much power

   (D) so that all of the states are represented

11 The fact that each state is represented by two senators means that—

   (A) the Senate is not as powerful as the House of Representatives

   (B) the House of Representatives has more to do than the Senate

   (C) the Senate has not been around as long as the House of Representatives

   (D) the number of senators for each state is not based on population

12 The notes taken by Aubrey suggest—

   (A) separation of power is a good idea

   (B) the most important branch of government is the executive branch

   (C) there should be more than three branches of government

   (D) there are not enough checks and balances in government

13 Where could Aubrey probably find more information to add to his notes?

   (A) in a dictionary

   (B) in a newspaper

   (C) in an encyclopedia

   (D) in a novel

14 George Washington, Abraham Lincoln, and Thomas Jefferson were all members of which branch of government?

   (A) executive

   (B) legislative

   (C) congressional

   (D) judicial

Selection 4 | Directions: Read the passage below and answer the questions that follow.

THE FLAG GOES BY

by Henry Holcomb Bennett

United nations heroes in the Flag Day parade during United Nations week, June, 1943. Oswego, New York.

Marjory Collins, 1912–1985, photographer.

HATS OFF
Along the street there comes
A blare of bugles, a ruffle of drums
A flash of color beneath the sky

HATS OFF
The flag is passing by
Blue and crimson and white it shines
Over the steel-tipped, ordered lines

HATS OFF
The colors before us fly
But more than the flag is passing by
Sea-fights and land-fights, grim and great
Fought to make and to save the State

HATS OFF
Weary marches and sinking ships
Cheers of victory on dying lips
Days of plenty and years of peace
March of a strong land's swift increase

HATS OFF
Equal justice, right and law
Stately honor and reverend awe
Sign of a nation, great and strong
To *ward* her people from foreign wrong

HATS OFF
Pride and glory and honor, all
Live in the colors to stand or fall

HATS OFF
Along the street there comes
A blare of bugles, a ruffle of drums
And loyal hearts are beating high

HATS OFF
The flag is passing by

Directions: Answer the following questions on your own.

1 **Which of the following is a "sign of a nation, great and strong" according to the poem?**

Ⓐ cheers of victory

Ⓑ equal justice

Ⓒ pride and glory and honor

Ⓓ loyal hearts

2 **Another good name for this poem would be—**

Ⓐ *The Marching Band*

Ⓑ *Victory Celebration*

Ⓒ *Along the Street*

Ⓓ *Pride of a Nation*

3 **Which line from the poem belongs in the empty box?**

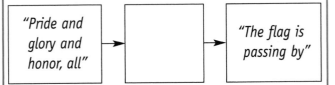

Ⓐ "A flash of color beneath the sky"

Ⓑ "Weary marches and sinking ships"

Ⓒ "A blare of bugles, a ruffle of drums"

Ⓓ "Blue and crimson and white it shines"

4 **Read the different meanings for the word *ward*.**

1. a room in a hospital

2. a child placed under the care of a guardian

3. open space enclosed by the walls of a castle

4. the act of guarding or protecting

Which meaning best fits the way the word is used in line 23?

Ⓐ meaning 1

Ⓑ meaning 2

Ⓒ meaning 3

Ⓓ meaning 4

5 **The scene being described in this poem is—**

Ⓐ a parade

Ⓑ a party

Ⓒ a battle

Ⓓ a concert

6 **Along the street "the bugles blare" and "the drums ruffle" because—**

Ⓐ everyone takes off their hats

Ⓑ the people are cheering

Ⓒ the flag is passing by

Ⓓ the band is marching

7 Which two lines from the poem mean the same thing?

Ⓐ "The flag is passing by" AND "The colors before us fly"

Ⓑ "Cheers of victory on dying lips" AND "Weary marches and sinking ships"

Ⓒ "Loyal hearts are beating high" AND "Sign of a nation, great and strong"

Ⓓ "Days of plenty and years of peace" AND "A flash of color beneath the sky"

8 Read the lines below that can be found in the poem.

"The flag is passing by
Blue and crimson and white it shines"

Is this an example of a fact or opinion? Explain the reason for your answer.

_____

_____

_____

_____

_____

_____

_____

_____

_____

_____

_____

_____

_____

_____

_____

9 What do you think the people along the street will do as the flag passes by them?

Ⓐ throw their hats in the air

Ⓑ take off their hats

Ⓒ hold hands

Ⓓ shake hands with one another

10 Why is the flag so important to the people mentioned in the poem? Explain what it means to them.

_____

_____

_____

_____

_____

_____

_____

_____

_____

_____

11 The phrase "HATS OFF" is repeated many times in the poem. What does this phrase suggest?

Ⓐ that it is a windy day and some people have their hats blown off

Ⓑ people are taking off their hats as a sign of respect and honor

Ⓒ it is a hot day and many people are taking their hats off

Ⓓ people take off their hats because they are sad and want to bow their heads

12 Which word *best* describes how the author probably felt when writing this poem?

Ⓐ sad

Ⓑ angry

Ⓒ proud

Ⓓ peaceful

13 You might expect to find this poem in a book titled—

Ⓐ *Fables and Folk Tales*

Ⓑ *Facts about Our Nation*

Ⓒ *Important Dates in History*

Ⓓ *Celebrating Our Nation*

14 What flag is being referred to in the poem?

Ⓐ the American flag

Ⓑ the Olympic flag

Ⓒ a pirate flag

Ⓓ a surrender flag

Theme Questions

Directions: The first theme of Section 2 was "Government by the People and for the People." Answer these questions. They are about the four Theme A selections you just read.

1 **Look at the chart Aubrey drew about how a law is made (page 80). In which step could Aubrey have written Thurgood Marshall's name?**

Ⓐ In step 1: "A bill is introduced in Congress."

Ⓑ In step 2A: "If a bill is first approved by the Senate..."

Ⓒ In step 2B: "...the bill goes to the president."

Ⓓ In step 4: "A law that is passed can be interpreted by the Supreme Court."

2 **How do the four selections support the theme "Government by the People and for the People"?**

_____

_____

_____

_____

_____

_____

_____

_____

_____

_____

_____

_____

_____

PART B: The 14 Essential Skills for Reading Success — All Together

3 How are the feelings that Mai had when she visited Washington, D.C. similar to the feelings of the poem, *The Flag Goes By*?

_____

_____

_____

_____

_____

_____

_____

_____

_____

_____

_____

_____

_____

_____

_____

_____

_____

_____

_____

_____

_____

_____

_____

_____

_____

_____

_____

_____

_____

_____

B Section 2: Independent Study

This is the second theme for Part B. This theme is also made up of four passages.

Theme B: The Attraction of Outer Space

Selection 1 | Directions: Read the passage below and answer the questions that follow.

NEPTUNE:
THE EIGHTH PLANET

Almost two hundred years ago some scientists began the search for a planet. At the time only seven planets were known to exist in our solar system. Uranus was the planet furthest from the sun. Scientists who observed Uranus noticed that it did not follow its predicted path around the sun. They believed something was causing this to happen. They thought it might be the gravity of a nearby planet. Using math they began to make calculations to help find the location of this planet. On September 23, 1846 a planet was observed in the sky in almost the exact place the scientists calculated it would be. This planet was named Neptune, after the Roman god of the oceans. It was the first planet to be discovered by using math. Eighty-four years later Pluto was discovered in a similar way.

The planet Neptune is the fourth largest planet in our solar system. Only Jupiter, Saturn, and Uranus are larger. If Neptune were hollow you could fit 60 planets the size of Earth inside of it. The planet is made of rock, water, and gas. Most of the planet is actually gas. In fact, it does not have a solid surface like Earth. When you look at Neptune you see the gases that surround melted rock and extremely cold water. A gas called methane gives the planet its blue color. Neptune is a very pretty planet to look at.

The weather on Neptune is very unusual. It has the strongest winds of any planet in our solar system. The wind can blow as fast as 1,200 miles per hour. On Earth it is called a hurricane if the winds reach a speed of about 70 miles per hour. It is also very cold on Neptune. The temperature there is close to -200°C. The main reason it is so cold is because of how far it is from the sun. Its average distance from the sun is almost 2.8 billion miles. This is over thirty times as far away as Earth is from the sun.

Like Earth, Neptune travels around the sun in an *orbit*. However, it only takes Earth 365 days to travel once around the sun. This equals one year on Earth. It takes Neptune 165 Earth years to do this! As Neptune travels in its orbit there are times when it is further from the sun than Pluto. So, the next time someone asks which planet is furthest from the sun stop and think before you answer. You will also need to stop and think how long one day is on Neptune. One day on Earth is 24 hours long. This is because it takes 24 hours for Earth to spin all the way around one time. Neptune only takes 16 hours to spin around once.

To see Neptune in the sky all you need is a good pair of binoculars. If you know where to look and the sky is clear you will be able to see a small dot. If you want a closer look you will need a telescope. In 1989 scientists sent the Voyager 2 spacecraft to Neptune for a very close look. They were able to learn a lot from the photos that were taken. For example, we now know that Neptune has at least eleven moons. The largest moon is named Triton. Triton is the coldest place in our solar system. The average temperature on this moon is -235°C. This is even colder than the planet Pluto.

In addition to moons, Neptune also has rings like Saturn. These rings are made up of dust and rocks. Some of the rocks are about the size of a car. There are four sets of rings around the planet. Not that long ago we were not sure if Neptune had any rings. But new telescopes and photos from the Voyager 2 spacecraft have made it possible to see them.

There is still much to learn about Neptune. The fact that it is so far from Earth makes it hard to study the planet. It is also very expensive to send spacecrafts like Voyager 2 so far into space. Still there are many scientists who think it is important to learn about this planet. We are learning more about our solar system each day. We should continue to learn about Neptune.

Directions: Answer the following questions on your own.

1 **Where is the coldest place in our solar system?**

Ⓐ Uranus

Ⓑ Neptune

Ⓒ Triton

Ⓓ Pluto

2 **This passage is *mostly* about—**

Ⓐ the nine planets in our solar system

Ⓑ one of the nine planets in our solar system

Ⓒ how a planet in our solar system was discovered

Ⓓ why exploring our solar system is important

3 **Which of the following happened first?**

Ⓐ Neptune was discovered

Ⓑ Pluto was discovered

Ⓒ scientists sent the Voyager 2 into space

Ⓓ scientists began to search for a planet near Uranus

4 **Which of the following best describes what the word *orbit* means?**

Ⓐ a straight line

Ⓑ two lines that cross

Ⓒ a path that comes to an end

Ⓓ a path like a circle

5 **Which of the following words *best* describes the weather conditions on Neptune?**

Ⓐ comfortable

Ⓑ peaceful

Ⓒ unpleasant

Ⓓ scary

6 **What causes Neptune to appear blue in color?**

Ⓐ water on its surface

Ⓑ a gas called methane

Ⓒ cold temperatures

Ⓓ strong winds

7 Describe two ways in which Neptune is different from Earth and at least one way they are similar to each other.

_____

_____

_____

_____

_____

_____

_____

_____

_____

_____

8 Which of the following is a fact?

Ⓐ Only Jupiter, Saturn, and Uranus are larger.

Ⓑ Neptune is a very pretty planet to look at.

Ⓒ We should continue to learn about Neptune.

Ⓓ The weather on Neptune is very unusual.

9 In the future scientists will probably—

Ⓐ prove that Neptune does not have any rings

Ⓑ prove that Neptune is colder than Pluto

Ⓒ send more spacecrafts to continue to learn about Neptune

Ⓓ not be able to learn any more about Neptune

10 Why does Neptune take less time than Earth to spin around once?

Ⓐ it is bigger than Earth

Ⓑ it spins faster than Earth

Ⓒ the winds are stronger on Neptune

Ⓓ at times Neptune is further from the sun than Pluto

11 You can tell from the passage that—

Ⓐ Triton is really a planet

Ⓑ Pluto is really a moon

Ⓒ Pluto is the furthest planet from the sun.

Ⓓ Pluto is colder than Neptune

12 The author of this passage probably believes—

Ⓐ it is dangerous for scientists to continue to study Neptune

Ⓑ it is important for scientists to continue to study Neptune

Ⓒ scientists are spending too much time studying Neptune

Ⓓ scientists will not be able to learn any more about Neptune

---

13 Explain why a newspaper would NOT be the best place to look for information if you needed to write a report about Neptune. In your answer name at least one source of information that would be better to use.

_____

_____

_____

_____

_____

_____

_____

_____

_____

_____

_____

_____

_____

_____

_____

_____

---

14 Which of the following is one reason why people could NOT live on Neptune?

Ⓐ The average temperature there is -200°C.

Ⓑ It is 60 times larger than Earth.

Ⓒ The planet was not discovered until 1846.

Ⓓ It takes 165 years to travel around the sun one time.

Jacob's Journey

Jacob was like most boys his age. He enjoyed daydreaming. No matter what he was doing, he always found his mind drifting. This was a real problem at school. Jacob was in constant trouble for not paying attention in class. Even at home, daydreaming got Jacob into trouble. When he was supposed to be doing his homework, he would stare out the window instead.

Jacob would dream incredible stories. He would start with a simple idea. As he made up the story, it would become more and more complicated. He dreamed of outer space and of times long past. He dreamed of places he had never been. Jacob dreamed of people he had never met. He would go on adventures to places he had never been before.

One day Jacob was sitting in a chair looking out his bedroom window. He sat and stared as the sun went down. When it became dark outside he looked up to the sky. It was a wonderful view. The moon and stars were bright. He began counting the stars After a few minutes he closed his eyes. Then a noise *startled* him. It was the sound of a loud engine roaring. He began to feel the chair beneath him shake.

He heard a voice, "Three, two, one."

Then he noticed a cloud of white smoke. Suddenly he was moving forward with great speed. Jacob realized that he was no longer in his bedroom. He was inside a huge spaceship and he was flying! He looked around. A large control panel wrapped around him. Switches and buttons flashed and blinked. He had a tight grasp on the flight stick that controlled the ship.

Jacob moved the stick a little bit to the left. The ship turned quickly in the same direction. He almost fell out of his chair. Then, Jacob moved the stick to the right. This time he made sure to brace himself. The ship turned just as fast to the right.

"Let's see what this thing can do!" Jacob thought to himself.

Jacob began to move the control stick in every direction. As he did the ship spun in circles and giant loops. After only a few minutes Jacob could fly the ship as well as any astronaut could. Soon he was on a journey to far away places that no one had ever seen before. He passed Mars, then Jupiter. Before long he shot past Pluto into the outer reaches of space. The stars were all a blur. He felt the force of the speed of the ship pressing him against his seat.

Jacob looked around the ship. Flipping levers and pressing buttons, he tried to figure out what each of them did. He noticed a flashing red button on the control panel. He thought for a moment then pressed the button. The ship raced forward even faster. It became difficult

PART B: The 14 Essential Skills for Reading Success — *All Together* for him to control. Out of nowhere, an asteroid appeared. Jacob tried to steer his ship away. He was too late. His ship hit the asteroid and spun in the opposite direction. He saw another asteroid directly in his path. He knew there was nothing he could do to avoid crashing into it. He braced himself for the impact. He began to shake back and forth.

"Jacob!" his mother called out. "Do you hear me? Is everything alright?"

"Everything is okay now," Jacob replied.

As his mother walked away Jacob smiled, closed his eyes, and leaned back in his chair.

Directions: Answer the following questions on your own.

1 Why did Jacob get into trouble at school?

(A) for fighting

(B) for being late

(C) for not paying attention in class

(D) for forgetting his homework

2 This passage is *mostly* about—

(A) a real journey into space

(B) a daydream that a boy has

(C) how a boy gets into trouble at school

(D) how a boy learns to fly a spaceship

3 Which event belongs in the empty box below?

```
┌─────────────────────────────┐
│    Jacob shot past Pluto     │
└─────────────────────────────┘
              ↓
┌─────────────────────────────┐
│                             │
└─────────────────────────────┘
              ↓
┌─────────────────────────────┐
│  Jacob's ship hit an asteroid│
└─────────────────────────────┘
```

(A) Jacob passed Mars.

(B) Jacob passed Jupiter.

(C) Jacob pressed the red button.

(D) Jacob almost fell out of his chair.

4 Which of the following words means the same thing as *startled* as it is used in this story?

(A) scared

(B) excited

(C) bothered

(D) enjoyed

5 Where is Jacob during most of the story?

(A) inside a spaceship

(B) in his bedroom

(C) at school

(D) outside his house

6 Why did the spaceship spin in circles and giant loops?

(A) It hit an asteroid.

(B) Jacob pressed the red button.

(C) It raced out of control.

(D) Jacob moved the control stick.

7 How was Jacob like most boys his age?

(A) He wanted to be an astronaut.

(B) He did not pay attention in class.

(C) He liked to daydream.

(D) He was in constant trouble.

8 Which of the following is an opinion from the passage?

(A) "He began to feel the chair beneath him shake."

(B) "The ship raced forward even faster."

(C) "Jacob would stare out of the window instead."

(D) "It was a wonderful view."

9 What do you think Jacob probably did after his mother left the room? Support your answer with information in the passage.

_____

_____

_____

_____

_____

_____

_____

_____

_____

_____

_____

_____

_____

_____

10 What can you conclude from reading this passage?

(A) Jacob can really fly a spaceship.

(B) Jacob did not really fly a spaceship.

(C) Jacob learned about outer space at school.

(D) Jacob just finished reading a book about outer space.

11 Read the sentence below from the passage.

"Soon he was on a journey to far away places that no one had ever seen before."

What do you think this sentence means? Explain where Jacob might be going and what he might see.

_____

_____

_____

_____

_____

_____

_____

_____

_____

_____

_____

_____

_____

12 The author of this passage probably thinks—

Ⓐ daydreaming is fun

Ⓑ children should be allowed to daydream in school

Ⓒ children should be allowed to fly spaceships

Ⓓ daydreaming is bad

13 This passage is an example of—

Ⓐ a magazine article

Ⓑ a biography

Ⓒ a script for a play

Ⓓ a fantasy

14 What time of day was it when Jacob was sitting in the chair looking out his bedroom window?

Ⓐ early in the morning

Ⓑ early in the evening

Ⓒ late at night

Ⓓ the middle of the afternoon

PART B: The 14 Essential Skills for Reading Success — All Together

Selection 3 | Directions: Read the passage below and answer the questions that follow.

Space Exploration Timeline:
1957–1998

October 4, 1957	The Soviet Union sends the first human-made object into space. It is a satellite named *Sputnik 1*. Information gathered by *Sputnik 1* is sent back to Earth by a radio signal. Three more *Sputnik* satellites are sent into space within the next year. One of them carries a dog named Laika.
November 26, 1958	The United States begins *Project Mercury*. The program has three goals: to launch a person into outer space; to learn what effect space travel might have on a person; and to safely return the astronaut to Earth. Over two million people work on the project for almost five years. Only seven astronauts are selected to fly into space. The astronauts fly into space inside a cone-shaped space capsule. The space capsules are about six feet wide and six feet tall. Each astronaut flies by himself.

Model of Mercury capsule used for wind tunnel testing, 1960. Courtesy of NASA.

April 12, 1961	Soviet *cosmonaut*, Yuri A. Gargarin, becomes the first man to travel into outer space. He travels once around Earth in a spacecraft called the *Volstok 1*. The ship is sent into space by the Soviet Union.
May 5, 1961	The *Freedom 7* carries Alan Shepard into space. He becomes the first American to reach outer space. His flight only lasts 15 minutes and 22 seconds, but he travels 116 miles above Earth. The capsule lands safely in the Atlantic Ocean.
February 20, 1962	The *Friendship 7* space capsule lifts off carrying John Glenn. John Glenn is the first American to travel around Earth inside a spacecraft. In less than five hours John Glenn travels around Earth three times.
December 4, 1965	The *Gemini 7* is launched carrying Frank Borman and James Lovell. The two American astronauts travel around Earth 206 times. Information from this mission provides proof that it is possible to travel to the moon.
February 3, 1966	The *Luna 9* is the first spacecraft to land on the moon. It is launched by the Soviet Union to gather information about the surface of the moon. This information is useful in planning future missions to the moon.

July 20, 1969  *Left to right: Neil A. Armstrong, Michael Collins, and Edwin E. Aldrin Jr., 1969. Courtesy of NASA.*	Neil Armstrong and Edwin "Buzz" Aldrin become the first men to walk on the moon. They travel to the moon as part of a three-man crew on *Apollo 11*. Michael Collins is also a member of the crew. During this mission samples of soil and rocks are collected from the moon. Neil Armstrong and Buzz Aldrin are on the surface of the moon for 2 hours and 24 minutes. The American crew safely returns to Earth on July 24, 1969.
June 19, 1976	The *Viking 1* spacecraft lands on Mars. Less than two months later *Viking 2* also lands on Mars. The two spacecrafts are sent to gather information about the planet Mars. One of their goals is to search for life. Each spacecraft has two parts—an orbiter and a lander. The orbiters stay in space and take pictures. The landers are able to land on Mars to collect soil and study the surface of the planet. Much information about Mars is gathered, but no proof of life is found.
April 12, 1981	The space shuttle *Columbia* is launched from Kennedy Space Center in Florida. John Young and Robert Crippen circle Earth 37 times in just over two days. The success of this flight is very important to space travel. The *Columbia* is the first spacecraft that can land like a plane and be used again for future missions.
June 19, 1983	Sally Ride becomes the first woman from the United States to travel into space. She travels on the space shuttle *Challenger* as a member of its crew. The shuttle remains in space for 6 days and travels around Earth 97 times. Following this historic flight many other women travel into space. Sally Ride goes into space again in 1984.
October 29, 1998	John Glenn becomes the oldest man to travel into space at the age of 77. He travels aboard the space shuttle *Discovery*. The crew of the *Discovery* performs experiments in space and gathers information. One of the greatest astronauts of all time is John Glenn.
November 20, 1998  *International Space Station (ISS) Concept, 1996. Courtesy of NASA.*	The first pieces of the International Space Station are brought into space by a Russian rocket called *Zarya*. Many different countries around the world agree to work together in building the space station. Some of the countries involved in the project include: the United States, Russia, Canada, and Japan. The construction of the space station is an important step in the future of space exploration. It is the first time so many different nations have worked together on a mission in space.

Directions: Answer the following questions on your own.

---

1 What is the name of the first spacecraft to land on the moon?

Ⓐ *Gemini 7*

Ⓑ *Luna 9*

Ⓒ *Apollo 11*

Ⓓ *Sputnik 1*

---

2 A good title for this timeline would be—

Ⓐ *Famous American Astronauts*

Ⓑ *Famous Firsts*

Ⓒ *Important Dates in American History*

Ⓓ *Important Events in Space Exploration*

---

3 Which event occurred between June 19, 1976 and April 12, 1981?

Ⓐ *Viking 1* lands on Mars.

Ⓑ *Viking 2* lands on Mars.

Ⓒ The space shuttle *Columbia* is launched.

Ⓓ The space shuttle *Columbia* returns to Earth.

---

4 A *cosmonaut* is the same thing as—

Ⓐ an astronaut

Ⓑ a spacecraft

Ⓒ a planet

Ⓓ a moon

---

5 The people mentioned in the timeline can *best* be described as—

Ⓐ famous Americans

Ⓑ talented scientists

Ⓒ brave explorers

Ⓓ ordinary people

---

6 Since Sally Ride traveled into space aboard the *Challenger*—

Ⓐ only men have traveled into space

Ⓑ many other women have traveled into space

Ⓒ no more space shuttles have been launched into space

Ⓓ she decided never to travel into space again

---

7 Which of the following is one way that a space shuttle is different from a space capsule?

Ⓐ A space shuttle can be launched into space.

Ⓑ A space shuttle can carry astronauts into space.

Ⓒ A space shuttle can travel all the way around Earth.

Ⓓ A space shuttle can land like a plane.

---

8 Which of the following statements is an opinion?

Ⓐ John Glenn is the first American to travel around Earth inside a spacecraft.

Ⓑ In less than five hours John Glenn travels around Earth three times.

Ⓒ John Glenn becomes the oldest man to travel into space at the age of 77.

Ⓓ One of the greatest astronauts of all time is John Glenn.

9 How has the *International Space Station* changed the future of space exploration? Use details from the timeline to explain how things might be different.

_____

_____

_____

_____

_____

_____

_____

_____

_____

_____

_____

_____

_____

_____

_____

_____

_____

_____

_____

_____

_____

10 What conclusion can you make about *Project Mercury*?

(A) It was very difficult to be selected as an astronaut for the project.

(B) Not many people were interested in working on the project.

(C) The *Sputnik 1* mission was the first step of the project.

(D) Many different countries worked together on the project.

11 You can tell from details about the space shuttle *Challenger* flight on June 19, 1983 that—

(A) Sally Ride traveled into space by herself

(B) Sally Ride was the first women to travel into space

(C) Sally Ride was not the first woman to travel into space

(D) Sally Ride had already traveled into space before

12 The main purpose of this timeline is to—

(A) provide information about events by listing them from most important to least important

(B) provide information about important events by listing them in the order they occurred

(C) provide as much information as possible about different spacecrafts used in the past

(D) provide information about the past that can be used to predict events in the future

13 Where would be the best place to look to find more information about the events included in the timeline?

(A) an encyclopedia

(B) a dictionary

(C) a newspaper

(D) a map of the stars

14 What would be one skill or ability a person would need to have to become an astronaut? Explain why this skill or ability would be important.

_____

_____

_____

_____

_____

_____

_____

_____

_____

_____

_____

_____

_____

_____

_____

_____

_____

_____

_____

Selection 4 | **Directions:** Read the passage below and answer the questions that follow.

A Letter to an Alien

Dear Mr. Alien,

I hope that you get this letter. Last week an astronaut came to visit our school. He told us all about space. It sounds like a really cool place to visit. Before he left I asked if he could deliver a letter for me. He gave me his address and said if I sent it to him that he would deliver it on his next space shuttle mission.

If you have read this far then I guess you have received my letter. My name is Jermaine Farnsworth and I live in a small town on a planet called Earth. In case you're not sure, that's the big blue planet with the white fluffy stuff in the sky. I live north of the equator between the Atlantic Ocean and the Pacific Ocean. In the town where I live there is a lot of tall grass and many trees. There are also a lot of animals. My family owns three cows, two horses, five pigs, eight sheep, and a few dozen chickens. Do you have chickens where you live? What about sisters? Are there any sisters where you come from? I have an older sister named Charlotte. She is always playing tricks on me. Last week she let the chickens get into my bedroom and make a terrible mess. It took me two whole days to get rid of all the feathers.

Where do you live? Mars?

I bet you live on a planet far away in another solar system. and just go to Mars for your vacation. I have never been to Mars, but I have seen some pictures. It seems like there are a lot of rocks and dirt there. We have rocks and dirt on Earth too. Maybe you should try planting a few flowers or some trees on Mars. Next letter I send I will make sure to include a *packet* of seeds. You'll be amazed how much nicer a few plants can make a place look.

I hope someday that I can travel to outer space. Soaring through outer space in a rocket would be so exciting! I would love to visit all of the planets, especially Saturn. Saturn is such a beautiful and amazing planet. I wish Earth had rings like Saturn. It would also be great if Earth had as many moons. I hear that Saturn has at least 18 of them, maybe more. Well, at least we have one. My sister told me that it is made of cheese. She also told me that there are little green people on Mars, but I do not believe her. You are not green are you? If you are it is okay. I was just wondering. Maybe you can send me a photograph of you and your family. Just make sure to put a stamp on the envelope before you send it. The mailman here will not deliver it without one.

I hope someday you will come visit us here on Earth. I am sure you would like it here. I can clear some room out back for you to park your flying saucer. My sister told me that is what you aliens like to drive around in. I bet they can go even faster than a jet plane or a rocket. My parents do not own a flying saucer, but they do have a car. It has four wheels, comfortable seats, and an engine that makes the car move. I do not have my driver's license yet. But if you visit I will let you ride my

My house

Earth

bike. It has two wheels, handlebars, and a not so comfort-able seat. Be sure to bring your own helmet in case mine does not fit you.

Well, I have to go now. I have some homework to do and it is getting late. Do they have homework on your planet? If they do and you ever get stuck on a question about Earth, just let me know. Maybe I can help. I know a lot about Earth and I get good grades at school.

Good-bye for now. If you are ever in the neighborhood please stop by for a visit. I will make sure to turn the porch light on so that you know which house is mine. Maybe we could look at the stars with my telescope and you could show me where you live.

Your friend from Earth,
Jermaine Farnsworth

Directions: Answer the following questions on your own.

1 Which planet is NOT mentioned in Jermaine's letter?

(A) Earth

(B) Mars

(C) Saturn

(D) Neptune

2 The main idea of the second paragraph in the passage is to—

(A) explain what animals are

(B) explain who Charlotte is

(C) describe where Jermaine lives

(D) describe the planet Earth

3 Which of the following happened before Jermaine wrote his letter?

(A) An astronaut delivered a letter to him.

(B) An astronaut came to visit his school.

(C) He had to do his homework.

(D) He turned on the porch light.

4 A *packet* can best be described as—

(A) a gardening tool

(B) an empty box

(C) a book about plants

(D) a small package

5 Describe Jermaine's sister, Charlotte. Use details from the passage and explain what Jermaine thinks about her.

_____

_____

_____

_____

_____

_____

_____

_____

6 What happened when Charlotte let the chickens get into Jermaine's bedroom?

Ⓐ The chickens made a mess.

Ⓑ The chickens chased Jermaine.

Ⓒ Charlotte had to clean up their feathers.

Ⓓ Charlotte played a trick on Jermaine.

7 How are Saturn and Earth different? Use details from Jermaine's letter to describe two ways that they are different.

_____

_____

_____

_____

_____

_____

_____

_____

8 Which statement from the letter would be considered a fact?

(A) "I hope someday that I can travel to outer space."

(B) "Soaring through outer space in a rocket would be so exciting."

(C) "Saturn is such a beautiful and amazing planet."

(D) "It would also be great if Earth had as many moons."

9 What is the astronaut least likely to do with Jermaine's letter?

(A) read it

(B) deliver it

(C) open it

(D) save it

10 Why does Jermaine suggest planting flowers and trees on Mars?

(A) He wants to prove that plants can grow on Mars.

(B) He wants to get rid of the seeds that he has.

(C) He hopes that it will make it possible for people to live there.

(D) He thinks that it would make the planet look nicer.

11 You can tell from reading Jermaine's letter that he—

(A) wants to live on Mars

(B) does not like living on Earth

(C) would like to become an astronaut

(D) has been inside a spaceship

12 What does Jermaine believe about space aliens?

(A) They only live on Mars.

(B) They probably do not live on Mars.

(C) They probably live on Saturn.

(D) They do not really exist.

13 This letter can *best* be described as—

(A) humorous

(B) poetic

(C) historical

(D) informational

14 Where does Jermaine live?

(A) in the city

(B) in the desert

(C) on a tropical island

(D) on a farm

Theme Questions

Directions: The second theme of Section 2 was "The Attraction of Outer Space." Answer these questions. They are about the four Theme B selections you just read.

1 **Where on the timeline in Selection 3: *Space Exploration Timeline: 1957–1998* would the first *Voyager 2* trip be?**

Ⓐ before *Sputnik* was sent into space

Ⓑ between the *Luna 9's* landing on the moon and the *Viking I* landing on Mars

Ⓒ after the *Zarya's* mission

Ⓓ before John Glenn's trip on the shuttle and after Sally Ride's travels

2 **How do the four selections support the theme "The Attraction of Outer Space"?**

_____

_____

_____

_____

_____

_____

_____

_____

_____

_____

_____

_____

_____

_____

_____

_____

3 There are true facts in both the story about Jacob's daydreams and the letter Jermaine wrote to the alien. What information in both of these stories is something that could have really happened?

_____

_____

_____

_____

_____

_____

_____

_____

_____

_____

_____

_____

_____

_____

_____

_____

_____

_____

_____

_____

_____

_____

_____

_____

_____

I Love Rayna

I Love Rayna